Phantom | Waters

Phantom | Waters

NORTHWEST LEGENDS OF RIVERS, LAKES, AND SHORES

Jessica Amanda Salmonson

SASQUATCH BOOKS
SEATTLE

Printed in the United States of America.
Distributed in Canada by Raincoast Books Ltd.

Cover photograph: J. C. Leacock
Cover and interior design: Julie N. Long
Composition: Fay L. Bartels

Library of Congress Cataloging in Publication Data
Salmonson, Jessica Amanda.
    Phantom waters : Northwest legends of rivers, lakes, and shores / Jessica Amanda Salmonson.
       p.   cm.
    Includes bibliographical references.
    ISBN 1-57061-018-5
    1. Waters—Northwest, Pacific—Folklore. 2. Lakes—Northwest, Pacific—Folklore. 3. Rivers—Northwest, Pacific—Folklore.
    4. Indians of North America—Northwest, Pacific—Folklore.
    I. Title.
GR109.5.S36   1995
398.2'09795'06—dc20   95-18588

Sasquatch Books
1008 Western Avenue
Seattle, WA 98104
(206) 467-4300

Contents

≋

Acknowledgments

A few of these stories have previously appeared in serial publications, and have been revised for this collection. "Ghoul John and the Corpse" appeared in *Isaac Asimov's Science Fiction Magazine,* edited by Gardner Dozois. "Young Man Who Became Weary" was in *Science Fiction Age,* edited by Scott Edelman. "When the Woman Chief Was Young" and "The Door to Rainmaker's Lodge" appeared in Ed McFadden's *Pirate Writings: Tales of Fantasy, Mystery & Science Fiction.* "Spirit Elk" was in W. Paul Ganley's *Weirdbook.* "The Shinbone Staff" was in Mark McLaughlin's *The Urbanite,* of Davenport, Iowa. My thanks are extended to all these editors.

Dedicative Introduction

≈≈≈

We are many of us mongrels in these United States, and I have always had a niggling pride in my pence-worth of Native American blood from my Cherokee-Yakama-Irish great-grandfather. In my tothood I was occasionally left with the Yakamas during seasonal fairs in which all my relations were participants. I must have looked very odd among the Yakamas, completely towheaded and pale. I was too young to have more than faint memories of those days. My strongest recollections of the Yakamas are of a very wrinkled old woman singing to me in her own language, and of escaping a fire in which my only pair of shoes became charred and ruined, so that I was barefoot the rest of the summer. Grampa by contrast, near whom I lived until he died when I was twelve, looms huge in all my childhood memories.

At some point I was naïvely convinced Grampa's stunning profile was one and the same as the image I saw on an Indian-head buffalo-nickel I kept as a magic charm. When I asked Grampa if that was him on my nickel, he assured me it was.

He was pagan through and through, yet when he sang "Old Rugged Cross," he could make a Christian out of a marmot, for when Grampa sang, his voice was as deep as the voice at creation. When he laughed, it was Thunder itself filled with mirth. When he wept, which was not often, it seemed to me the very earth was falling away.

He told me many tales of his adventurous life. Some I recall, many more I've forgotten, though they have all served to inform my subconscious in remarkable ways. While some of what Grampa told was not true, all of it was entertaining, and to me he was a great man. His steel mill union activities alone would qualify him as a legitimate hero, and as it was Grandma and my great-aunts who revealed that part of his history, it came to me without the storyteller's exaggerations. It was nevertheless the stuff epics are made of.

While still a young man, Grampa left the Northwest and became a Mississippi riverboat gambler. Because he was handsome, and because he smoked four packs of Lucky Strikes a day, he was once asked to be a poster boy for the cigarette company. He threatened the life of the company's representative, smashed the gold watch the man had gleefully placed in his hand, and never smoked another day in his life.

In Illinois, he met my English great-grandmother, Elva Couch. She'd had one misfortune in love, which caused her to be shamed by her upper-crust family. For this she had been designated the "resident old maid," whose duty it would be to nurse elderly relatives, one after another, into the grave. She chose Grampa instead.

The wealthy Couches promptly disowned Elva, whether for marrying Irish or Indian is hard to say. Grampa brought her to Washington State, where her personal dowry bought a piece of land from the Burlington Railroad. From this land I used to walk along a forested canyon stream all the way to Puget Sound, so that water ran through my childhood as evocatively as it runs through the stories of this book. In all, five closely overlapping generations were to live on that land before it was, over time, parcelled away to nothing.

~~~~~~

I have inherited from Grampa a romantic disposition. I have an interior certainty and knowledge of a beautiful age that all outward evidence tells me never did exist. For this reason I am drawn to Fantasy and Folklore as the best way of expressing what I know instinctively is true, whether or not science and history support me. The wonderful thing about folklore is that it reflects a people's own romanticization of itself, in the old sense of "Romanticism," wherein every emotion and event is heightened and idealized in its perfect terror or its perfect beauty.

Folklore therefore regards equally the good things of the soul and those things that are to be abhorred. And the wonderful thing about retelling legends is how the act of retelling proves each tale's continuing dynamism for successive generations, assuring us our souls are still intact.

My pence-worth of native blood is not what qualifies me to have borrowed this mix of Indian and white legends of Northwest waterfalls, rivers, bays, lakes, and shores, with which to fashion short stories to varying degrees my own. My main qualifications are a profound respect for the storytellers who have come before me; a love of the Pacific Northwest, where I was born and to which I will one day be joined ashes to earth; an expansive amount of research and devotion to my subject; and an artist's desire to have invested something of my own into these traditions—something worthy of dedication to Grampa Perry, whom I hope one day to meet again in a country greatly resembling the unblemished Northwest of long ago, near the lodge of Tyhee Saghalee.

—JESSICA AMANDA SALMONSON
Seattle

The Ruined Idyll

A Legend of Multnomah Falls

TWO BROTHERS, STRONG young men, were sons of Speelyi the Coyote. They lived in an age when the divine animals were losing their supremacy, and humanity was a still-young race of giants.

The elder brother was proud and cruel. He delighted in battle and was rebellious at heart. He wore a grizzly pelt and a cougarskin cap. He bore with him at all times a copper sword and a warclub. The sword was short and broad, a single piece of beaten metal flared behind the grip, which was wound about with sharkskin and bound with tendon. The warclub was inlaid with teeth of obsidian and was longer than the sword. The club he carried across his back; the sword was strapped to a belt of elk leather.

The younger brother was mild of heart, a poet who sang songs of a prophetic nature. He wore a shirt of braided mountain-goat wool and an artfully patterned apron of woven roots and cedar bark. Because he was fond of catching salmon, he had with him at all times a fishing spear with a notched spearhead made of elkhorn. The shaft of the spear was carved with totemic animals representing the mysterious ancestors of these giants, the first of men.

These two fell in love with the same woman, whose name was Wahseakli, the Sorceress. She was a delicate young giant who wore pelts of ermines and whose wild cascade of hair was as white as the foaming waters of Cascade Rapids. Her mother was Moon; her father was Rain. She ran like a wild deer through the forests. She carried a quiver full of arrows, and the quiver was made from the hide of a white deer, its arrows fletched with the white feathers of a swan.

The warrior wooed her daily, performing heroic deeds to impress her, but he did not fail to praise her for her own skill with the bow and arrow. "Huntress and hunter!" he said. "We are two heroes created for one another!" And as he strutted mightily, the white-haired maiden felt truly she could never love another, for who in the world was stronger or more brave?

The younger praised her with poetry, sung in a sweet voice. His compositions were of a musical language. His every word impinged upon Wahseakli's thoughts and lingered long after he had spoken; and Wahseakli felt she could never love another, for who in the world had so beautiful a heart?

It was not possible to choose between two such suitors. When the brave warrior told her of his exploits, his eyes flashed like those of Thunderbird, so caught up was he in the moment. She was swayed to him, and he believed he saw in her devoted gaze the evidence that he was destined to be chosen. Then the younger would come and woo her with his lovely words, and she would blush with the feeling that such sensitivity must in the end take precedence over brute strength and aggression.

During the day, she could be seen flitting through the forests with her bow and arrow as she led the bolder of her two beaus on a merry chase, filling the bright sky with a tinkling laughter in which might be heard the promise of an everlasting love. That same evening, she could be spied lying in the moonlight, sighing like a dove, absorbed in the younger beau's sweet compositions. The people who lived along the Chukallilim River, which was later called the Columbia, thought the threesome had become much too notorious, and Wahseakli's indecision made her appear fickle. The people blamed the captivating sorcery of Wahseakli for making the two men silly.

~~~~

Speelyi the Coyote dwelt along the upper Chukallilim, where he fished and hunted in seclusion. There were no settlements of the new humanity in that region as yet, and sometimes he felt he needed not to see such people. He had himself taken the form of a man with a coyote's head. He sat in his canoe, gazing at the ten fingers of his hands, and thought that the form of a human was useful for many things. But he well knew that his heart was not human. He was Coyote, a demigod. His willful nature far exceeded humanity's selfishness. There were times when he did not like humans and was keen to punish them, even if it was true that the first of them had sprung from his seed. Speelyi knew that the future belonged to human people, not to animal people, and this is why he played tricks on them and let them suffer.

As his kind was more and more displaced by humanity, and as Speelyi's rule of the world slipped from him by slow degrees, the old trickster became increasingly insistent upon having his way, on using his powers to enforce his personal will without regard for others. There in his canoe on the upper river, he pondered the useless lives his sons had been living. The gossip had reached him even in this secluded place. Activities of sons reflected upon a father. He would not have it!

He paddled downriver and called his sons to him. He remonstrated with them. "You are living ineffectual lives. You share the same obsession. You are like birds mesmerized by a serpent."

The Ruined Idyll

The brothers sighed, and said as with one voice, "She is no serpent."

Their silliness enraged Speelyi, but he remained outwardly at ease, knowing that his actions might drive them further into this madness. Calmly, he said, "She must be domesticated, or neither of you will establish a clan of your own. You have spoiled Wahseakli too much. As it is now, she will never choose. Come, let us confront her at once."

As each brother was convinced he alone was favored, the two went eagerly with their father to the cavern on the high cliff wherein Wahseakli lived. The day had long been overcast because of Speelyi's bad mood, and it started to rain. Yet as they approached the cliff, Speelyi called to the sorceress in the cavern, raising his arms so that sunlight opened the clouds. A rainbow swept across the scene. Wahseakli thought Speelyi had brought the sunlight and rainbow to honor her, so she came out of her cavern. But soon she was alarmed to discover his mood severe.

"You must end your wild ways and choose between my sons," said Speelyi.

"I love them both," said Wahseakli, and the brothers, hearing it, batted at one another playfully behind their father's back.

"You will marry one, or I will pronounce a doom upon them both," said Speelyi. As he spoke, thunder rolled in the distance. He said, "I did not sire them to be the pets of a wildwoman."

Hearing their father's threat, the brothers lost their playful feelings. They exchanged worried glances. Perhaps indeed things could not continue as before.

Wahseakli well knew the power of these old ones who lingered from the animal days. She gave a sigh that sounded like resignation. She said, "Come, take me in your canoe, away from my lovers, so we can speak honestly."

He took her in his canoe, in the belief that she had become reasonable. But she was only biding her time while she planned her escape. As the canoe drifted under a low branch of a tree that overhung the bank, she grabbed the limb and drew herself up. Speelyi took hold of her ankle and yanked her back into the canoe with such force that it smarted. He kept hold of her foot. The back of the hand that gripped her had become hairy like a coyote's paw. He demanded with a growling voice, "Choose at once!"

His manner so angered her, she could not help but answer just as meanly. "My ancestors were heavenly beings, but my suitors are the sons of a dog-headed man. It will never be that a falcon marries into the family of a dog!"

Speelyi drew back in alarm. Who had ever insulted him so? It took a moment for him to respond, for he was unused to such words. A low, menacing growl began to build in his throat. His teeth were bared. Wahseakli realized she had overstepped herself. She leapt upward into the overhanging tree just in time to evade Speelyi's raking fingers.

Speelyi dashed after her along the banks of the river. Wahseakli turned and unleashed arrows as she ran, firing backward over her shoulder. Speelyi caught her arrows in his teeth and gnashed the shafts to bits. Wahseakli climbed the cliff to the crest of the mountain. Speelyi caught hold of her streaming white hair and shoved her to the ground with cruel determination, intending murder.

Below the cliff near the river, Speelyi's sons had begun to war against one another. The elder brother bore his warclub in one hand and his copper sword in the other. In the younger brother's spear was magic sufficient to deflect the stronger weapons. Upon his poet's lips were insults so artful that his brother became too enraged to fight well. Indeed, it looked as though the younger brother might win against the stronger man, for his spear had the longer reach.

Seeing his sons at such a pitch, Speelyi thought it best to separate them in the way he had often done when they were children. So that Wahseakli would not escape him while he saw to his sons, he lifted a boulder and set it on her hair, much of which was left hanging over the cliff. Wahseakli kicked and cried out, but she could not move the boulder. Speelyi then rushed down the face of the cliff and with a mighty spring forward snatched the younger son's spear in his teeth, stopping it in midflight. The younger brother had been that close to winning.

The elder brother was crestfallen. He knew in his heart his life was saved, but he was unwilling to admit there was ever a moment when his weak brother could have slain him. He turned at once upon his interfering father. In an unfilial rage, he cried out, "We were happy until you disapproved! I will raise an army to war against you! I will skin you and wear your pelt!"

The younger added, "Who else than you is the author of our sadness? I join my brother. I will use my oratory skills to awaken hatred for you among all people."

Hearing these threats, Speelyi gnashed his teeth until his gums frothed with blood. All fatherly feeling was spent, and godly retribution came to the forefront of his mind. He grabbed his warrior son by the throat and heaved him upward, turning him into a towering rock that would never again run in the forest or canoe along the river, but would forever after stand firm. He would hear the wind free at his head and the river free at his knees, going ever on without him.

Speelyi then turned on his other son and thrust him away mightily. The young poet was flung to the opposite bank of the Chukallilim River. Where he landed, he too turned to stone.

Then Speelyi returned to the sorceress. She had nearly dug herself out from under the boulder. A moment before she was free, Speelyi fixed his foot upon her hair, near her scalp. "If I lift my foot," he said with wicked pleasure, "you will tumble from the cliff!" But rather than demean herself by begging, she turned her face and sunk her teeth into Speelyi's ankle with such an awful bite that he howled and hopped away. As she began to tumble from the cliff, she was transformed into a waterfall, her white hair becoming a wonderful high cataract possessing all the seductive charm that had once belonged to Wahseakli the Sorceress.

When Wahseakli's spirit tried to flee to her parents' lodge in the sky, Speelyi snatched her out of the air and imbedded her soul in the wall of the cliff, behind the waterfall, whence mournful cries of loneliness can still be heard in the roar of the falling waters.

~~~~~

A traveller along the Columbia River Gorge will see a sight of such unsurpassed beauty that the cruelty of Speelyi might nearly be forgiven. The older son is Castle Rock, among the world's largest natural monuments, in which dwells the soul of a great warrior of a bygone age. At the opposite bank is Rooster Rock, the poet who still holds such power of prophesy that knowledge of the future is imparted to any who climb upon the rock or pass it on the river.

As for Wahseakli, she is now called Multnomah Falls, the highest falls along the river, leaping nearly one thousand feet from Larch Mountain. She possesses all the enchantment and beauty of her former self. In the harsher winters, when the plunging waters form great slender heaps of white, translucent ice, Wahseakli, daughter of Moon and Rain, reappears as a lovely pale figure clad in ermine garments.

The Legend of Chief Patkanim's Spies

A Tale of the Snoqualmie River

TODAY BUSES BRING loads of eager tourists to Snoqualmie Falls. As the people file out of their transports, a great many head for the Salish Lodge lookout at the top of the falls to observe the tremendous waters raging forth from craggy high cliffs. The bolder portion take the winding rustic trail to the base of the falls, in order to stand within sweet mists and dream of long-lost days when in every corner of the Northwest there was unspoiled beauty such as this.

Sometimes someone cries out, convinced they see a bow, a quiver, an arrow's shaft, or a decorated piece of bark armor adrift in the whirling eddies near the shore. But as they approach, the relic resolves into a twig or a half-rotted board. Others have reported visions of men thrashing helplessly in the roiling caldron, or pale drowned corpses bobbing about beneath plummeting waters. But such visions invariably resolve into imagination.

Here, then, is a tale of long ago, to ponder on your next venture to the falls.

~~~~

Rumor spread throughout the Snoqualmie Valley that the Yakamas, together with other tribes east of the mountains, were planning a raiding party through the valley to Puget Sound, to punish Snohomish and Snoqualmie villages for refusing to participate in the multitribal war against the whites. The peoples of the west side of the Cascade Range had heard these threats often enough, when Yakamas would say, "Join us to exterminate the interlopers, or you will die with them!" With mountains separating their nations, such threats were rarely taken seriously.

Chief Patkanim lived at a permanent camp with bold men on Whidbey Island in Puget Sound. When the rumors reached Patkanim of the Yakamas' impending raids, he set out with his warriors in canoes. From Whidbey, they crossed the sound and paddled up the Snohomish and Snoqualmie rivers toward a rendezvous in the Snoqualmie Valley. Patkanim and his men, provisioned by white settlers at Holmes Harbor, were armed with long knives and rifles.

When the chief's canoes reached their destination, Patkanim called together a tribal council in the lower valley. He said, "Upper-valley Snoqualmies have intermarried with the Kittatas Yakamas for many generations. Some of you Snoqualmies who sit with us, I am sorry to say, are not wholly to be relied upon. Because there are spies among us, I require that during this crisis, Snoqualmies refrain from visiting the mountain pass. You must not speak of our plans even to your sisters and wives, who may chance to repeat information to east-of-mountain women living here on the west side."

From among his closest warriors, Chief Patkanim selected his two finest Snohomish scouts. He said, "Go spy on the Yakamas while pretending you are friendly Snoqualmies!" His spies set out at once. As they approached the summit of the lower fork of the pass, they detected the odors of fires and horses from a camp of Yakama warriors.

The two spies crept upon the scene. From a high wooded place, they observed that the Yakamas had gathered together a sizable war party. As horse riders, Yakamas knew very little of the ways of the west-mountain canoe peoples. It was possible, with some difficulty, to lead horses over the rougher part of the pass. But a war party from the eastern plateau could not hope to come upon forest tribes by horse, as they would be detected from a long way off. The Yakamas therefore planned to leave their horses at the camp and rely on Snoqualmie guides to get them through the pass. They were even now in the process of preparing a dozen large canoes for a downriver raid.

The Snohomish spies had to suppress laughter on seeing how poorly the canoes were outfitted. Weapons and supplies were arranged in an unbalanced way, and the boats were much too large to maneuver well on smaller rivers. The Yakamas had doubtlessly traded buffalo rugs for the river crafts. They had gotten the worst of the bargain, for they were not expert in judging the quality of boats. They had not been provided with finer examples of canoe workmanship. Even the paddles appeared to be the "poor tries" of boys still learning to carve.

Keeping as straight-faced as possible, the two spies sauntered into the camp. At first they were challenged by the Yakamas, until they greeted the warriors in a friendly, easygoing manner. One of the spies claimed relationship to a certain Snoqualmie man who had a Yakama Kittatas Valley wife; the other claimed his late grandfather had been a man of the Kittatas. These lies were easily accepted, for the Yakamas were from a place beyond the Kittatas Valley and did not know the Kittatas families well. The spies, pleased that their subterfuge so easily passed scrutiny, smiled broadly while introductions were exchanged.

There were, however, six Snoqualmie men in the camp. They might have contradicted the spies if they dared. They looked ill-at-ease and did not carry weapons. The two spies boldly greeted them as fellow tribesmen. The six fretful Snoqualmies went along with the

The Legend of Chief Patkanim's Spies

pose. One of the spies leaned close to a Snoqualmie and whispered in Salish, "Are you working as their spies, bringing harm to our valley?" The man replied, "We were living east of the mountains and were forced to serve as scouts." The spy said, "Keep silent, then. You had better volunteer to take care of the horses when the braves head out for the raid. My friend and I will be their scouts from now on."

Then the two spies wheedled their way into service as river guides, making extravagant claims about their expertise on the complex network of creeks and tributaries. "We will lead you straight down into the lower valley. No one will expect us," boasted the spies. And they encouraged the warriors to crowd into the twelve unfit canoes.

Meanwhile, Chief Patkanim gathered a carefully chosen group of Snohomish braves and led them upward by way of the lower fork of the pass. A scout came to the chief and informed him of a hostile camp at the summit. When Patkanim and his men arrived, the camp was mostly abandoned. "The braves have gone down the river by canoe," said another scout. "They have left six Snoqualmie lackies behind, with three armed Klickitats to watch over the Snoqualmies. There are no Yakamas presently in the camp. They have gone downriver to cause grief, but I think they are already lost. I found a spot where they dragged their boats out of the Cedar River and carried them to the wrong tributary. Our spies must be with them, leading them astray."

With a good idea of how things were progressing, Chief Patkanim and his braves swiftly surrounded the camp. The half-dozen Snoqualmies made no excuses and offered no resistance. Finding themselves outnumbered, the three Klickitats made a run for their horses, but Chief Patkanim's men were in the way. The foes were disarmed and dragged before the chief, while the Snoqualmies stood nearby looking sheepish for their part in things.

The chief asked only a few well-chosen questions, by which he quickly perceived the breadth of the situation. As the six Snoqualmies had never been convinced the raid was a good idea, and had been impressed against their will for the mission, Chief Patkanim released them.

As for the Klickitats, the chief drew forth a long knife, and with three swipes he beheaded them. Then he called to two of his warriors, saying, "Take these heads and a canoe and make your way back to the settlement the whites call Holmes Harbor. Give the heads to the whites as a gift from Chief Patkanim, so they will be reassured that our people can patrol the aggression without the need of white force."

And so it was done.

~~~~

The Yakamas' raiding party continued on its way into the valley by canoe. Because the mountain peaks were obscured by clouds, the Yakama warriors could not judge in what direction they were headed. Twice the guides told the warriors to get out of the canoes and carry them, first to a big creek and then to a broad tributary. Most of the Yakamas were young. The leader of the party was a strong, severe warrior who had hand-selected his men specifically because they had no family connections with those Kittatas Yakamas who had intermarried with Snoqualmies. This was so that no man would feel disinclined to kill the enemy; but it also meant they knew nothing of the layout of the land. If the war chief had brought a few Kittatas men with him, he might not have had to rely so completely on the two guides.

Thus far, the raiders had not encountered a single village, though the mountains were supposedly dotted with settlements. Still, suspicions were not yet aroused.

The Legend of Chief Patkanim's Spies

The Yakamas left a sedate tributary and entered the quickening waters of a larger river, the spies informing them that this was the river they had sought. At first the horse warriors were alarmed by the rapids. They felt sick from having rocked all morning in canoes that rode low in the water. Each vessel sat from eight to twelve braves whose complexions were looking more and more like the faces of green goblins.

The guides, who were in the lead canoe, set a difficult pace. They cried out from time to time for all the canoes to stay close together and follow precisely. They shouted, "If any canoe goes too far left or right, it will be dashed to pieces among the rocks! Warriors will be swept away to drown! Stay close! Stay close!"

This was hardly reassuring to warriors accustomed to flat country and calm waterways. They'd like to see the situation reversed, with river men bucked off the backs of Appaloosas.

It was a terrible ride. Some Yakamas madly bailed water out of their canoes using nothing but their hands. The regalia of their war dress had become soaked from splashes and spray; the feathers of their warbonnets hung thick with damp. They used paddles in an awkward and worrisome struggle to hold a course between rocks as they were swiftly carried along by raging, frothy currents.

Even the great trees of the ancient forest began to oppress them, like hovering, living monsters with their crowns shrouded in mist. In the plateau country were pines smaller and farther apart, whereas these mountain firs were disapproving God Trees that seemed to glower at the raiders.

As the river widened, the fearful rapids calmed. The warriors gave a collective whoop of joy, their spirits much lifted. They paddled out-of-time, striving to keep the canoes in the middle of the river and on course.

They went in a crooked line, one behind the other. Word was sent along the line of canoes from the guides in the lead canoe, encouraging the parade to hold as close together as possible. "It will be easy from here on! But up ahead, the river will get narrow for a little while, so stay close! If you lag behind, you may get caught in an evil current and dashed on the rocks!"

Staying close together in the coming rapids was the most perilous thing they could do, but horse warriors knew nothing of that. They were sweating and worn out because they were unused to so much paddling. Still, the going was much less rough for the time being, and they kept themselves in high spirits, trusting their guides' knowledge of the river, for there was never a moment when the guides seemed worried about the waters. The Yakamas began to jest of the wicked violence by which they planned to punish the Snohomish and Snoqualmies who would not join in the great fight against white intruders. The spies listened to jests about cruel acts, and had to force themselves to laugh along.

Soon the river narrowed. Rocks poked up everywhere. The headlong rush became even more harrowing than the earlier part of the journey, if such a thing was possible. Smiles of relief gave way to visages that were once again tight with fretful concentration. Over the raging noise of the river, they could barely hear the reassuring words from the guides. "Stay close! Right through here! It gets easy after this!"

But it did not get easy. Spouts of water shot upward on all sides, like aquatic demons with white, roaring faces, striking at them as their canoes sluiced clumsily between wet, green boulders. Unexpectedly, the two guides stood up in the lead canoe, rocking it as they leapt together onto a large rock. One of them nearly fell into the rapids, but the other caught him just in time. They stood side by side on the slick rock like motionless specters watching twelve overfilled canoes speed by them into the most horrendously violent waters imaginable!

The rapids leapt over rocks like huge, frothing serpents, shoving the canoes this way and that. Within moments of passing their guides on the rock, the Yakama warriors saw what lay ahead, and the sight of it increased their terror. Panic showed upon their faces as they began to paddle backward as fast as their weary arms would let them, but this slowed them not in the slightest as the boats shot headlong through the roiling waters.

Several men leapt from their canoes into the river, sinking instantly from view. Four of the twelve canoes overturned. The heads of the warriors reappeared only once or twice before sinking away, never to resurface. The remaining warriors wedged their knees against the walls of the canoes to hold their places, lifted their paddles or their spears above their heads, and unleashed a collective cry—a great shout that was nevertheless not loud enough to be heard over the roar of Snoqualmie Falls, as the whole of the raiding party was launched downward into death!

The Phantom Ship
A Legend of the Seattle Waterfront

THIS CITY THAT is like a dream never ceases its surprises. One rainy afternoon in Seattle autumn, with the wind so high that an umbrella would have been useless, I found myself approaching the waterfront in search of someplace dry. A train blocked my path before I could cross to Alaskan Way. I stood in the blowing rain getting wetter and wetter, and feeling ornerier and ornerier, as the train poked by.

At last I crossed to Pier 70, but I was by now so drenched it seemed pointless to seek shelter in the import shop that dominated the businesses in what had been, a couple decades before, an old dock warehouse.

My mood was as sour as the weather as I leaned against the dock railing and watched the sharp rain pierce the surface of the water. I felt so awful that I simply didn't care about the rain. The evil mood crept upon me so firmly that it came into my thoughts as a desire to leap into the icy waters of Puget Sound and do away with all the mediocrity and disappointments of life.

Having just suffered a useless interview for a stupid job, I felt an utter failure in the world. I had stooped to consider cocktailing in the lowest of low dives on a run-down block along Western Avenue, and had actually been rejected from such demeaning work. It was thus that Dame Gloom wrapped me in her cold, dank cloak.

Out of the corner of my eye, I perceived a man standing farther down the dock, clad in a peacoat and captain's cap, and as drenched as I was. I had been a volunteer at a downtown shelter for a couple of months earlier in the year, and had gotten to know many of the city's homeless, but this man I did not know. As he approached me, I braced myself to be panhandled. The homeless are so despised, so used to unfriendliness or indifference, that I felt I would have to speak to him, though I was in no mood for it. I'd have to explain in all honesty that my unemployment insurance had run out and I had no idea where I was going to get this month's rent. Unless my luck changed soon, I might end up sitting beside him in the mission, awaiting a free meal.

But he was not a panhandler. He spoke to me in a rough but quiet voice, saying, "Don't worry about the rain, my pretty doxy. There's always the sun behind the clouds."

I was unexpectedly moved by his odd sincerity, so much so that I lifted my gaze from the water's surface. I expected to see a grizzled, grandfatherly face. To my surprise, he was relatively young, his trimmed beard void of grey, though he seemed old in his expressive eyes and in his weather-worn features.

He turned away from me and began walking toward the far end of the pier. Wind and mist whipped around him. He faded from view, as though he had stepped into fog. Only—there *was* no fog, and I stood with mouth foolishly agape, staring at the space where the ghostly captain had vanished.

~~~~~

Two years later, life had improved for me somewhat, even though dark moods haunted me periodically, with or without good reason. For much of that period I had been selling my handmade jewelry in the Pike Place Market, managing, however marginally, to make ends meet on my own terms. After a lull in business for the Market crafts-people, which always occurs for a few weeks in autumn, crowds had begun to build again, working their way toward the major Christmas crunch. I'd unexpectedly had a lucrative day shortly after Thanks-giving, and I was feeling momentarily wealthy.

After dark, having packed away my stock, I invited Karen, a fellow marketeer who sold silkscreened sweaters, to join me for dinner. I hadn't splurged on a fancy meal in a long time, and a local jazz group was playing for a minimal cover at Pier 70. "My treat!" I enthused, which naturally increased Karen's eagerness.

The shops inside the converted pier-warehouse were closed evenings. We passed through a dark outer hallway behind the main import shop, lingering only a moment to look at miniature books in the display window of one the smaller shops, and then continued to the restaurant at pier's end.

Karen and I were guided to a window seat looking onto Puget Sound. It was perfect. Our waiter—a young man with a tragic coun-tenance—brought us ales. We sipped then as we awaited our seafood orders, watching the lights of passing ships far out on the water.

The atmosphere was warm and pleasing; the music was good and not too loud for conversation. I said to Karen, "I have kind of an affec-tion for this pier. Despite the tourist shops, it's still rustic and feels as though it's steeped in Seattle history. A couple years ago, I seriously pondered leaping off this very pier."

"What! Why?"

"Oh, unemployment, bad love life, postmenstrual blues; who knows? I'd heard the water's so cold, even a strong swimmer lasts only about a minute and a half, and it's totally painless. It seemed a good idea at the time."

The Phantom Ship

"So what changed your mind?"

"A ghost."

Karen laughed and squinted at me askance.

"Really. A sea captain. Looked like a bum. He called me his 'pretty doxy' and then vanished into mist. He had such an air of tragedy about him, yet he told me there's always hope. It didn't exactly cheer me up, but I started to figure my own life couldn't be *that* bad. If even a dead guy could look for the bright side, then so could I. Though I can't recall the exact day, this might well be the second anniversary of my not dying."

"You're teasing, aren't you?" Karen asked incredulously.

I guess I had a foolish smile and looked like I might be spinning a tale. I turned away from Karen's puzzled expression to look out the window. A shimmering mist was gathering just off the end of the pier, like a slowly whirling pillar of fog lit from within. "What the devil's that?" I wondered aloud.

By the time Karen looked, the shimmer had become the merest wisp of fog. It blew over the end of the pier, dissipating.

"It's him," I whispered hoarsely. I don't think Karen heard. There stood a man in a peacoat, leaning on the railing, his back to the pier's building. It could have been anyone, but I was sure it was my captain. I said, "Wait here, Karen, I'll be back in a minute," and gave her no further explanation.

I'd left my coat inside, and the air was chilly. The salt-scented wind blew back my hair. By the time I made it to the far end of the dock, there was no longer anyone there. But on the sound, just north of the pier's tip, a shadowy clipper ship loomed upward in the darkness.

The weird ship's bowsprit reached nearly to the place where I was standing. Incongruously, its tall masts were at full sail, though the chill wind did not affect its stationary position. There were no lights on board and, what is more, the lights of the city seemed to be absorbed into it. The apparition was so faintly visible I could have easily doubted my senses.

As I gazed dumbfounded at the ship, so near I might have leaned across the rail and touched the bowsprit, I caught sight of a phosphorescence on the dock to my left, at the very edge of my vision. When I turned to look at it directly, the strange patch of fog had coalesced, pulsing with its inward light. Then it drifted through the rail of the dock to alight on the deck of the phantom ship.

The clipper ship began to draw away from the dock, with no sound of water at the hull. I heard only the muffled jazz from inside the restaurant, the lap of salt water at the pier's pilings below, the faint sounds of the nighted city and cars on the Alaskan Way viaduct . . . but from the ship itself, there was absolute silence.

Then, as the ship drew away into the night, I saw atop the prow the young-old man in peacoat and captain's hat gazing at me. His lips were thin and firm within his short beard. He raised a hand, whether in greeting or farewell I did not know, and I found myself raising my own to wave back.

~~~~~

Moments later, I was again seated across from Karen. "What were you doing out there?" she asked, for she had seen me through the wide window.

"Did you see it?" I asked. "Did you see that ship?"

She looked up to observe a well-lit ferry in the distance. I knew by her expression that she hadn't seen the clipper ship. At that moment our waiter leaned over the table with our plates. He had heard my query. He was a thin, pale young man, with long, delicate

The Phantom Ship

hands and large, sad eyes. As he set my plate before me, he momentarily leaned closer, speaking softly and conspiratorily so that Karen couldn't hear over the band. "Only the melancholy among us ever see it," he said.

Karen broke the moment, saying, "I'd like another ale please," and I added, after the waiter's querying glance, "None for me, this is fine."

I watched his back as he walked away. I felt a camaraderie with him, for we shared the curiously reassuring certainty that there *was,* beyond this sad world, something graver, greater, and deeper than we shall ever plumb in life.

The Spirit Elk
A Legend of Lost Lake

)))

PLAIN FEATHER KEPT a deermouse in his shirt. On quiet after-
noons, he would sit outside his lodge on Dog River and take the deermouse out of his shirt. It was red-furred on top, white-furred on the
bottom, and had dainty feet. The deermouse was exceedingly tame,
and liked to climb to the tips of Plain Feather's fingers, its tail
wrapped around his thumb, from which perch it was pleased to be
fed grass seeds and young crickets. Sometimes the deermouse
chirped at Plain Feather as might a bird.

About that deermouse, Plain Feather was sentimental. But when
it came to bear or elk, he could be merciless. No one could track
game as well as this man. Even so, when he invited someone to hunt
with him, Plain Feather never sought the credit for what was killed.
Also, if his family had plenty of fish and roots and berries, he was apt
to forgo the hunt altogether, or to catch only an unimpressive squirrel
or a goose to vary the family repast.

Overall, he was a humble man, and he lived almost as quietly as
his deermouse. He was devoid of presumption and was never known
to brag about his abilities. Those who best knew him understood perfectly that there was nowhere a more skillful hunter. Had he elected
to do so, he could have made a great name for himself. Many young

men said to one another, "If you or I possessed even half of Plain Feather's skills, we would be great braggarts, and prove our boasts by consistently bringing home the fattest brown bears, the swiftest deer, and the mightiest of elk. We would drop our kill before the doors of our lodges with a great fuss and racket so everyone would notice. But what does Plain Feather do? He plays with a mouse. Is he not great in his humbleness?"

The reason for Plain Feather's retiring ways was something he never discussed. It was generally understood that he led his life in accordance with the wishes of a personal guardian spirit, but the nature of that spirit was unknown save by Plain Feather himself. Not until the last day of his life did he tell the people about the Spirit Elk.

When he was a young man, Plain Feather went to Lost Lake, where he fasted and prayed until the Prince of Elks came to him. This supernatural animal was twice the size of an ordinary elk, and its eyes were as red as fire. As the elk spoke, Plain Feather listened in quiet awe. "I will be your spirit guide throughout your life, but only with the provision that you respect all life, no matter how small, and never kill more than is required for your immediate need."

When he awakened from his trance, Plain Feather spied a wet and pitiable deermouse in the lake, clinging to a piece of floating bark. It looked so cold and miserable that Plain Feather's heart was touched. He took a long twig and reached out to the deermouse. The timorous beast was a youngster, and so grateful to have found a savior that it was instantly affectionate. That deermouse was the great-great-great ancestress of the deermouse Plain Feather possessed at the end of his life—for in all his days, he kept such a small thing as a reminder of the commandment of his guardian spirit.

~~~~

Sharp Fox was the assistant of a tribal doctor. He thought himself an important fellow, for one day he too would become a doctor, if he lived so long.

He did not have a pleasing disposition. Somehow he got it into his head to dislike Plain Feather. He became jealous, for it seemed to him the hunter was always winning unearned praise. Whenever Plain Feather was first to return from a hunt, with most of his arrows still in his quiver, Sharp Fox railed against him. "You quit the hunt with so many arrows left? A true hunter does not stop until his arrows are spent!" But Plain Feather put his quiver under a bench in his lodge and ignored Sharp Fox's huffing.

Sharp Fox urged a few rowdy young men to pester Plain Feather. "Hey, old man, let's go on a hunt for fun! No? Too old for the forest!" Then they would walk away laughing. Plain Feather said to himself, "I am not so old as to deserve to be called an old man. But I am not young like those rowdies, either." To be chided as not up to the hunt stung him like a bee. But he bore the abuse, for at least the opinion of rowdies was not widely held.

Having failed to annoy Plain Feather sufficiently to cause him to change his manner, Sharp Fox slowly came to understand that the hunter lived a life of obedience to a guiding spirit. This very realization increased Sharp Fox's jealousy, for if he were ever to become a tribal doctor and not just an assistant fetching things, he would require a guardian of his own.

Several times Sharp Fox had tried to find a guardian. But he could never fast more than a day, because when he was hungry he could not resist the berries and roots the forest offered. Nor did he like to stay long in the forest, especially if the weather was bad or bears were about. He had a suspicion the spirits didn't like him. Why should the spirits like Plain Feather so much? What had Plain Feather ever done to deserve the love of spirits and the admiration of people? He said to himself, "Why, that hunter is so stupid, he doesn't even realize he has an enemy!"

Somehow or another, Sharp Fox promised, he would find the way to make his enemy break his vows to his guardian. He plotted in the darkness of his heart, devising a method by which to defeat Plain Feather. First he waited until the tribal doctor was on a trip to meet with fellow doctors who lived farther down Dog River. Then for two days he pretended to be asleep. His family shook him, but he remained still. When the two days had passed, he came out of his lodge, saying he had dreamed a powerful dream.

"Wontulat the Supernal Chief came to me in my dream. He said, 'Sharp Fox, you must save your people! The coming winter will be harsh. The snow will be this deep. Many will freeze to death, and those who remain will starve. But this can be averted if you will tell the hunters to go into the forest at once and kill as many animals as possible, so that meat can be dried before the snow comes.' Then Wontulat the Supernal Chief walked away from me, across Dog River."

Hunters set out in force. They laid bets with one another on who could kill the most animals. They began to kill everything they saw, each striving to prove that he was the mightiest of the hunters.

Plain Feather did not join the sport. His heart was drawn toward the contest, it was true, for gambling was his weakness. He well knew that he could easily win. Even so, he resisted, remembering the vow the Spirit Elk had extracted from him when first he came to manhood.

The good hunters were just as glad not to have to compete with him. But the young rowdies chided him that he had forgotten a lifetime of tracking skills; or his legs were too stiff to travel far; or his eyesight was no longer good enough to shoot even a rabbit brought to him in a box. These barbs hurt, but he turned away without response.

Sharp Fox came to him and said, "Great Wontulat said, 'Kill as many animals as is possible.' Why have you not listened? Do you want our people to starve this coming winter? You haven't the sense of a duckling's pinfeather! If even one child dies for lack of meat, you will be blamed."

Finally Plain Feather went out. He followed a lone deer back to its herd; then he killed twenty deer with twenty arrows. He needed assistance bringing all the carcasses home. He found the young rowdies, who had made so much noise in the forest that they'd had no luck hunting. They agreed to help him and went with him to fetch the slain deer. How they sang his praises! They took the meat into the village, calling to the people to see the results of an extraordinary feat. Plain Feather felt himself puff up with pride. All his life he had denied himself this pleasure. Everyone was in awe of him—even the rowdies who formerly called him old.

The next day he killed five black bears and a grizzly. The women went into the forest to dress the meat. As they worked, they sang a new song about the greatest hunter in the world, whose name was Plain Feather of the Wascos. People were talking about petitioning the chief to give Plain Feather a more heroic name, such as True Arrow or Shoots Fast. The hunter swelled up just to know he was uppermost even in the thoughts of the chief.

Urged on by increasing praise, Plain Feather let the young men follow him the next morning. He closed his eyes, nocked his arrow, and shot into a tree. Two squirrels fell out of the tree, pinned with one arrow, and Plain Feather had not even broken his stride. All day long

The Spirit Elk

he killed things, big and small, always with an effortless twang of his bowstring.

In the afternoon, his chorus of toadies grew weary of cheering him on. Carrying fresh carcasses back to the village, they left Plain Feather alone. When they did not come back, he felt abandoned, but he said to himself, "What do I care for praise? I am a mighty hunter! Is there not a bloodlust upon me? What is this track? A band of elk! And that track there. Another band of elk! Ah!"

In all, he spotted the spore of five bands of elk. He came upon the first band and unleashed arrows. Five does with their young, and a mighty buck, were thrown into a frenzy, unable to scent their foe or ascertain which way to flee. The buck leapt straight up and was taken by an arrow through the throat. He did a midair somersault and came down, crushing his antlers. Plain Feather ran forth to pile up the meat, then, noting where he left the carcasses, hurried to the next band, and the next.

He scurried this way and that, silent as a ghost, leaving a trail of death. He slipped amidst the shadows of the trees so quietly he surprised even a fox, and, since his arrow was already nocked, he killed it. As for the number of elk he'd slain, he lost track.

As he crept upon the fifth and final band, a twig snapped under his moccasin. The does leapt away, followed by their fawns, but they did not get far. Plain Feather's arrows chased after them without error. He killed them in swift succession; they were struck in mid-leaps and fell kicking as they died.

He had one arrow left. Only an unusually large female remained. She stood her place and looked straight at him without flinching, without running away. She was strangely beautiful, with shimmering white fur the likes of which Plain Feather had never before seen. He thought what splendid garments could be made from her remarkable fur. He would wear her skin at festivals! He would wear her skin in winter, and people would say, "Look there, the snowdrift has come alive and is handsome!"

It never for a moment occurred to him he might miss. One arrow was always sufficient. And true to form, the glistening obsidian arrow-head cut into the hide of the enormous doe and sank deep enough to find the heart.

Miraculously, she did not fall dead. She leapt over bushes and into the thick forest. Evidently, the doe was so muscular that the arrow had not pierced as far as the hunter had presumed. Even so, she must collapse soon. Plain Feather followed after the doe, waiting for her to fall.

Deeper and deeper into the darkening forest he was led by the wounded animal, past piles of elk, over the corpse of a fox, a rabbit, a bear, an eagle, and other things he'd killed that day. When he had covered sufficient distance and there was no longer evidence of hunting, Plain Feather thought to himself how admirable was the elk's strength. Just at dusk, he arrived at a beautiful little lake, the very one where, years before, he'd had his vision of the Spirit Elk.

Mount Hood was a shadow against the falling night. Bats sprang from the forest in great numbers to swoop among the clouds of gnats over the lake, a vision fading into dusk.

The elk was lying in shallow water, weak and panting. Plain Feather waded out to grab the expiring animal and pull her ashore. But when his hand took hold of her by the ear, the elk drew him swiftly to the middle of the lake. He tried to let go of her, but could not. The elk was sinking, and Plain Feather was drawn beneath the water.

For a moment he lost consciousness. When his reason returned to him, he was standing in a forest at the bottom of the lake. All around him were the spirits of deer, elk, bear, squirrels, geese, rabbits, and a red fox who looked at the hunter with a judgmental gaze.

A commanding voice called out, "Bring him to me!" The animal-spirits nosed at him until he was forced into the presence of the Elk Prince. This elk, bigger than a moose, lay on his side. His antlers were like an oak in winter. His hide was pierced all over with arrows, and blood seeped from him into the lake-waters, curling away in carmine ribbons like wisps of smoke from a fire. All those arrows were fletched in the way that Plain Feather had learned from his father.

The Spirit Elk said, "Why have you disobeyed? All these are the spirits of animals you slew unjustly. For every arrow you unleashed without need, the spirit of that arrow has found me. I can no longer be your guardian spirit." Then the Spirit Elk rose to his feet with difficulty. He lifted his head to trumpet angrily, "Cast him out!" The animal-spirits nudged Plain Feather upward and toward the shore.

In the morning, Plain Feather awakened on the shore. He was sick at heart. He reached into his shirt, but his deermouse was not there. Then he saw on the lake, lying on a piece of bark, the pathetic little corpse of his pet. She must have drowned while Plain Feather was under the water. Wailing with grief and regret, he reached out with a twig and pulled the piece of bark to him. He broke the bark in two and made a tiny cedar coffin bound together with vine. He climbed into a nearby tree and set the deermouse coffin into a hollow formed at the crotch of a divided trunk. The whole while he sang an inspired song: "I am burying my soul, I am burying my soul."

Plain Feather returned to the village weak and weary. The tribal doctor had discovered the lie of his assistant and had killed Sharp Fox, whose body was displayed on the trail. Plain Feather went into his lodge and lay down. He called his family to him, and many friends, and he told them the story of his guardian spirit, finishing with his confession. "I have been in the place of lost spirits. I wounded my guardian spirit, the Prince of Elks, and in so doing have lost my soul. Now I must become a ghost that dwells with the spirits of beasts that are unjustly slain."

When he died, his soul went into the Lake of Lost Spirits, in whose clear surface the face of Mount Hood is reflected.

Ghoul John and the Corpse

A Tale of Sauvie Island in the Lower Columbia

}}}

THERE WAS A white ghoul who travelled along the Columbia River in the 1830s. His name was John. There were, by then, increasing numbers of white ghouls, and Ghoul John was famous among them for his ghoulish pursuits. These creatures called themselves "relic hunters." The people stood guard by their burial grounds, which in past ages, when there were no white ghouls, required no guards.

One day white ghouls came to Memaloose Island, the place of the thirteen sacred death lodges. Men and women ghouls piled out of their excursion boat, wearing fine garments and hats and carrying picnic baskets. They chittered among themselves gaily. The men strutted in high boots. The women swung parasols and stepped daintily. They were such happy ghouls.

Their plan was to eat the food they had brought along, and when their baskets were empty, they would refill them with the flathead skulls of babies. But the people were ready for them. They fired a volley of balls over the heads of the white ghouls, who ran back to their boats in a hurry-scurry. The lady ghouls complained most of all, because their picnic and relic-hunting excursion had been spoiled by savages.

Had Ghoul John been with them that day, it would have been

harder to frighten them away. He was a tricky ghoul. Everyone knew about him. The people watched his every move. He was a lazy ghoul and hated to use a paddle, so he asked among the people for assistance, hiring two big men to paddle him about in a canoe. These two men were able to keep a particularly close watch on Ghoul John's activities, so the people could rest a little easier until he was gone.

It was Ghoul John's method to ride a big ship up and down the Columbia River. At various creeks and estuaries, he would tell his hired people to take him upstream by canoe, claiming he only wanted to look at burial places. "I would never do anything offensive," he promised the people. "Would I risk the good will of the people?" But to his fellow ghouls, he said, "For my own part, I would be willing to take any risk to procure those skulls. But I am restraining myself on account of the ship and crew, who might suffer from prejudice if my sacrilege were discovered."

Wherever he landed, about twenty of the people would show up, pretending to do this or that, surreptitiously keeping watch. On one burial island, Ghoul John walked around with his fingers twitching. Spittle frothed at the corners of his mouth, so eager was he to desecrate the graves. He felt deprived because he was so closely watched, and the people could see how greatly Ghoul John suffered.

When Ghoul John finally got in the canoe and was taken back to the ship, an old woman of the people came forth to the burial ground. She was a woman of great medicine. She walked about the graves, waving her wand over the bones to purify the ground Ghoul John's feet had polluted and to cleanse the air where Ghoul John had breathed. Standing on the ship, Ghoul John watched the purification rites with an attitude of weird delight.

Ghoul John went downriver to White Ghouls Settlement on

Wapato Island. Fort William, as the ghouls called the settlement, was established by a shipmaster named Nathaniel Wyeth. This island, some fifteen miles in length, with its own lakes and streams, had always belonged to the people. In an out-of-the-way place along a certain stream, there was Chinook holy ground that remained in active use as a place for the dead.

Ghoul John insisted he must see the holy ground. He was taken up the stream by the hired people. "How thrilling!" he said, clapping together his pallid hands. When his hired people gazed at him, he found them worrisomely inscrutable, so he tried to disguise his excitement with a more respectful demeanor. His guides restrained him from getting out of the canoe, and warned him not to disturb the ghosts. As he had no other ghouls with him, Ghoul John was pliant.

From the canoe in which he knelt, he could see, about a hundred feet away from the stream's bank, a stand of sacred trees in which canoes were mounted high in branches. Each canoe had a smaller canoe laid atop it, upside down, forming a lid. How Ghoul John hungered to lift the lids! He said to himself, "I must return here in secret this very night. I must have what's in those coffins!"

At midnight the ghoul went out from the fort and climbed into a little canoe by himself. He paddled along the island, close to the bank, until he came to the creek, and then he paddled up that. Soon he came to the stand of trees that had so captivated him. He ran his canoe into the shallows. The canoe could not reach the beach, so Ghoul John took off his boots and waded to the bank.

He approached the coffin tree.

His heart was beating wildly. He had a feeling of excitement in his groin as he climbed into the tree and lifted the canoe lid. His grinning face shone in the moonlight. He was deliriously happy. "Oh! Oh!" exclaimed Ghoul John. Laid out in the canoe was a young woman, wrapped in very fine blankets, who had died two or three years earlier. The oils of the coffin's cedar wood had preserved the woman's body. She was dried out and stiffened, but her body showed no sign of decay. "Oh!" exclaimed Ghoul John. "A perfect mummy! I must have her!"

Most white ghouls beheaded corpses for their flathead skulls. It was not uncommon for the people to find one of their sacred burial grounds desecrated, with all their dead relations beheaded. But Ghoul John was overcome with love for the dead woman. He wanted to take her away with him in her entirety, to possess her intact. So he tied a rope around her and lowered her to the ground. He replaced the canoe lid so that his deed might pass undetected. Climbing out of the tree, he strapped the dead woman to his back, and with leaps of joy he hopped barefoot through the shallows to his boat.

Now Ghoul John fretted that the two large people he had hired would discover what he had done. If they found the woman's corpse, they would surely take her away from him. So he took her into the fort and hid her in the storehouse of another white ghoul, whose name was Walker. He told Walker, "I deposited my prize in your storehouse. I have sewn around her a large Indian mat, so she looks like a bale of guns." Ghoul Walker agreed that this was terribly clever.

Because the people were aware of Ghoul John's perversion, he knew it was not safe to take the mummy with him when he left the following day for Fort Vancouver. He instructed Walker to send him the mummy on the next schooner. Walker was agreeable to these matters, and said he would be happy to commit such a crime on behalf of his good friend Ghoul John.

Several days later, Ghoul John hurried down to the river to meet the schooner newly anchored off Fort Vancouver. He pranced along the river's edge, clasping his fingers as he sang, "Where's my mummy? Where, oh, where's my pretty mummy?" But to his distress, there was no mummy on board. Instead, the captain handed him a letter from the ghoul called Walker. From this letter Ghoul John learned the reason for his disappointment.

The dead woman's brother, Lean Elk, lived at Cascade Rapids, near the place where the Old Ones made paintings and carvings on the faces of the rocks. On the night his sister's grave was robbed, Lean Elk suddenly awoke in his lodge. Standing at the foot of his bedding was a four-inch replica of his sister. Her soul had entered the lodge without waking anyone but Lean Elk. He sat up amidst warm furs and observed that the miniature of his sister shone like a star. She looked extremely sad. Before Lean Elk could address her, she popped out of existence, like a bubble on the river.

Early that morning, Lean Elk set off down the river for Wapato Island. He paddled up the creek to inspect his sister's canoe. He came to the coffin tree and saw that her canoe had been shifted. He visited her often, to bring her small gifts, to sing to her spirit, to speak to her of the things that were going on in their family, or to boast of his luck fishing, just as he had done when she lived. Being so greatly familiar with her resting place, even a slight change could not pass his eyes unobserved. With a sinking suspicion in the pit of his bowels, he climbed up and looked under the lid.

Although he remained outwardly calm, in his heart he was in a panic. He came down from the tree and looked more closely at the thief's footprints. They did not turn inward like those of people, but turned outward like those of white ghouls. He knew at once this was the work of Ghoul John. He went to the fort and set his case before the one called Walker.

At first Walker tried to brush the matter off, but Lean Elk would not listen to lies. He looked right into the pale eyes of the ghoul when he said, "The people watched Ghoul John leave, and he had no opportunity to take my sister away from this fort. Please, where have you hidden my sister?"

It is surprising to note, but there are some ghouls who experience pangs of guilt, especially when looking into the eyes of one of the people. By and large, ghouls are liars who bunch together with a common lie, which becomes for them the truth. Walker might easily have stuck to his lie, but looking into the dark eyes of a man, even a ghoul can be awakened to humanity. Sorry for his assistance to Ghoul John, and fearful that the people might be sufficiently outraged to kill some ghouls, Walker not only returned the mummy to Lean Elk, but gave him, as well, nice blankets in apology.

Then Walker sent the letter to Ghoul John. He wrote, in part, "The poor Indian took the body of his sister upon his shoulders, and as he walked away, grief got the better of his stoicism. The sound of his weeping was heard long after he had entered the forest." And even today, if you listen, if you are sensitive of heart, you will hear, in the wooded places around Sauvie Island and along the banks of the Columbia, the sound of Lean Elk weeping.

The Girl Who Loved the Forest

The Legend of Lake Sutherland

§§§

Out in the woods where the air is sweet,
And the fragrant, wild things blow,
Dwelt you and I from the world apart
In the beautiful long ago.

—ELLA HIGGINSON

NAHKETA'S FAMILY LIVED in the mountains of the northern Olympic Peninsula. She was the pride of the Klallam tribe. All who saw her loved her for her innocence, naïveté, and sweetness. Her people felt for her a loving protectiveness. They sheltered her in such a way that she grew to young maidenhood never knowing pain or sorrow.

She was as tender and gentle as a fawn, with a voice like a rippling stream that flows through meadows. She loved the forest as though it were her brother; she did not believe in its dangers. A falling mist was to her a warm blanket. Even when to others it was cold, Nahketa stood laughing in the rain. The wind soughing through the branches of the trees spoke to her in a mystical language, and the words all conveyed to Nahketa the reassurance of her well-being.

The beauty of the woodlands astounded her with its explosion of ferns, soft carpets of mosses, and trees in greens of every shade, spiced here and there with the rust red of cedar bark, dappling clouds of wildflowers, and yellow speckles of mushrooms.

In the early misty autumn, Nahketa and her sisters and mother and all the women of the tribe wandered the forest gathering medicinal herbs. Nahketa plucked an herb here, pulled a root there, placing each wonderful discovery into her woven basket. Her mother, a famous herbwoman, had taught her the lore of the flora, so she was highly selective, and filled her basket slowly.

Toward dusk, she realized she could no longer hear the women singing. She had wandered far afield, failing to keep track of where she was in relation to her village. She called out to her sisters, but her voice died in the deep shadows of the forest. She called to her mother, but there was no reply. Still, having never known fear, Nahketa strode onward, as brave as always, certain that in time she would stumble upon the correct path.

It grew dark and still she was not worried. She heard the owls calling, and though she knew they had the voices of ghosts, she was certain that her brother the forest would protect her. She ate some of the contents of her basket and enjoyed her feast, though the roots were tough and raw.

Nahketa grew weary as the night progressed. Her legs were scratched and sore. With high spirits and kindly feelings, she lay beneath the curve of a big fallen tree, pulled leaves about herself for a semblance of warmth, and hugged her sweet-scented basket of herbs as she fell asleep, dreaming a strange and beautiful dream of her marriage with the forest.

~~~~~

For four days the Klallams searched the forest for Nahketa. Her mother and sisters were frantic. The whole of the tribe scoured the landscape, searching farther and farther, calling out to her night and day, "Nahketa! Nahketa!" The only reply was the mystic soughing in the branches and the rippling of the streams.

Some said a forest-spirit had taken her away to be his bride, for she had always been enamored of nature, and the forest must have loved her too. But on the morning of the fifth day all hopes were dashed. She was found lying beside a log, her body torn open by a wild animal. Even so, upon her visage was a look of peaceful beatitude, causing some to suppose she had died of exposure to the cold well before the wild beast mutilated her corpse.

Nahketa was buried in the place where her people found her, together with her herb basket, her mother's finest blanket, and a few small objects for which in life Nahketa had had sentimental feelings. All the rest of the day and deep into the night, the grieving tribe sang dirges and beat mournful drums around the campfires of their village. Her sister's aching fists pounded the earth. Her mother's wails rose to heaven.

The enormity of the tribe's grief must have touched the heart of Tyhee Saghalee, who watches from the sky. Upon the dawn, as the cries of grief faded and the aching, mournful rituals came to a close, the people saw that a lake had sprung from the place of Nahketa's death and burial. All along its shores stood ghostly white-barked alders.

The Klallams thereafter called the lake Nahketa. In time it was renamed Lake Sutherland, after the first white man to set eyes upon such loveliness. But Nature herself recalls the true name of that place. Down to our own day, in the chilly autumn, when the leaves of the alders turn to lace upon the forest floor, birds can be heard as they glide over crystal wavelets calling with high shrill voices, "Nahketa! Nahketa!"

The Girl Who Loved the Forest

The Woman Who Turned to Soap

A Tale of Lake Crescent

"An old legend has it that Lake Crescent never gives up its dead. The Klallams would never cross it by canoe. They said there were evil spirits that reached upward with icy claws to drag down anyone who tried to fish there. Until 1957, the lake was commonly thought to be bottomless; many grew up in Port Angeles believing that was a fact. It was finally sounded at six hundred twenty-four feet at its deepest point, and that's plenty deep enough."

The waitress seemed to have taken her break specifically to fill me in on the local lore. She had overheard me introducing myself to the bartender as "Penelope Pettiweather, intrepid Northwest folklorist and ghost detective." He'd laughed, glad enough to meet an eccentric old gal with an interest in strange things, but he couldn't add much to my store of notes. I hadn't seen the young woman as the bartender and I spoke, but when I sat down at a table with a Roy Rogers and a grilled cheese sandwich to peruse my field notes, the waitress sat across from me and said, "You're the woman who writes books of spooky stories for kids?"

"Well, not necessarily for children, but I must confess I do write about odd things now and then. Call me Penny."

"Hi, Penny, glad to meet you," she said, offering me a hand across the table. She didn't introduce herself. "Are those notes about the soap woman?"

"Some are. Do you know anything about her?"

"Sure." She lit up a cigarette. I wished she hadn't, but you can't criticize someone who's about to volunteer sought-for information. She said, "I kind of relate to her in a weird way, you know what I mean? I think she wants her story remembered. She doesn't want to be forgotten. I've sort of taken it as my duty to keep her memory alive. I look like her a bit, don't you think?"

"I haven't seen a photo of her yet. I plan to spend the night here at the lodge and check local newspaper morgues and libraries tomorrow. Then I suppose I'll see some photos."

"Take my word for it, she and I could be sisters," she said, and leaned back in her seat. She blew smoke rings toward the ceiling, which rather impressed me despite my disapproval of smoking. My friendly waitress continued: "Hallie Illingsworth had auburn hair and piercing dark eyes. She was a big strong woman—not unattractive, mind you; but it couldn't have been easy killing her, I'll tell you that; she would have put up a devil of a fight. If not for a lucky blow, it might have been a husband rather than a wife that went into the bottom of that lake. So, what do your notes say there?" She was trying to read my scrawls upside down.

I lifted my notes. I began to read a fragment: "1940, afternoon of July 6—Lake Crescent for the first time returns one of its dead."

"You've got that right," she interrupted. "The first and only time. The day she resurfaced, the lake was smooth as a mirror and the deepest blue imaginable, fading toward shore to a polished turquoise. There was this guy named Louis Rolfe in a fishing skiff with his brother. Louis spotted an oblong object and pointed it out. His brother asked, 'What the hell is it?' It floated near the rocky wall that leads to Sledgehammer Point. It looked like a human body wrapped in a gray-striped blanket. Louis turned the skiff about and hurried to the dock of the state trout hatchery, where he told the superintendent what they'd seen. 'Shorty' Immenroth laughed it off at first, said it was probably a deer. Nevertheless, he went out on the lake with Louis. There on the crystal-clear water, Shorty saw the outline of the object, a pure white shoulder showing through a tear in the blanket, and an alabaster foot dangling from one end of the bundle, a piece of rope tied around the ankle.

"It was a fact—she'd turned to soap. The lake is fed continuously by Olympic Mountains snowmelt. When you're six hundred feet down in frigid water, you don't rot. You're preserved, that's what, and saponification sets in. That's what it's called. Saponification. It means that after the cold stopped the decay, salts in her system changed all her fatty tissues little by little, and she turned to soap. She was down there for three years at forty-four degrees Fahrenheit, just exactly what the process required. Because the soap was lighter than the water, she came to the surface. The transformation must have happened to past corpses too; all of them must have turned to soap. So you might ask yourself, Penny, why only this one came to the surface, especially as she had been tied to something to weigh her down. There's more of a mystery there than people realize."

Her voice had lowered, and I found myself leaning forward, despite her smoky breath, eager as I was for her perceptions regarding the mystery. She paused and waved the cigarette about, evidently appreciating how she had put me at the edge of my seat. Then she took up her narrative again.

"Even after all that time in the depths, she was still recognizable as a strong, good-looking woman, her auburn hair hanging thick and wet. She was taken to a mortuary. The mortician and the cops found her to be as shapely as the day she was tossed in, not a speck of rot, a clean neutral smell coming off her. An elastic garter was still on one leg and she wore fragments of a green dress. As the soap was soft, she had undergone some damage when she was transported. Part of her face as well as her toes and fingers were gone or damaged.

"They put her in a potter's field grave. Fourteen months later the case broke, thanks to dental records distributed to five thousand dentists throughout the USA. A dentist of Faulkton, North Dakota, remembered the partial plate that had been kept as evidence. His records reminded him he'd made the plate for one Hallie Spraker. It didn't take long after that to find out who she'd married and that she'd disappeared from her Port Angeles residence on December 3, 1937. Hallie Illingsworth's fool husband must have known the day would come when his crime would be found out. He served nine years of a supposed life sentence before he was paroled, then disappeared, probably with an assumed name.

"All this is a matter of public record. But there's one little piece of the puzzle still missing. That's the matter of the lake allowing her to return. When someone drowns in that lake, their corpse is never found. Never. So how did Hallie come back? Perhaps it's because the lake didn't kill her itself. It doesn't take offerings, it only takes lives."

I could tell by her manner that she had told me pretty much all she intended to, and her break from waitressing was done. As she stood, she told me, "There's an old geezer comes in here now and then, name of Benjamin White, lived in the area all his life. You should go and talk to him."

~~~~~~

Benjamin was retired and a widower. The thing he liked best to do was fish. He'd been a fisherman since he was a child, when his father took him on outings to lakes and streams far and near. Yet Benjamin would not fish on Lake Crescent, though it was the nearest place and was famed for a unique species of trout. I sat in his livingroom, notepad on my lap, listening to his story.

"Those Klallams weren't stupid; they knew their business. It's a damn strange lake. I was fishing there once when I was a young man. I'd sooner be tarred and feathered than fish there again.

"I'd gone in the early hours, well before sun-up, to a place up near the Sledgehammer I'd had a feeling about. I remember it was the second morning after Independence Day. There'd been crowds along the beaches two days before, setting off firecrackers, hardly helpful to a fisherman. Now most of those people had left. The stragglers were asleep at their campsites. There was a sliver of a moon and a passel of stars for company. The lake was so quiet, I lay back with my line in the water and fell plum asleep right there in my boat. The next thing I knew, I was having the damnedest dream.

"I was walking on the bottom of the lake. Six hundred feet down, they say; there I was, just walking along light on my feet, easy as you please. I didn't feel wet or cold or anything but lightfooted. It was hard to keep my feet on the bottom. Everything was glowing blue so that I could see perfectly well. There, all about me, were old skeletons, their skulls grinning as I strode by. Near some of the skeletons were arrowheads in little heaps, as though a couple centuries had made quivers and arrows dissolve, leaving only the flints. One skeleton had an antique pocket watch on a gold chain dangling amidst the ribcage.

"Then I came to a body that was standing straight up and was not at all decayed. It was a tall woman wrapped in a blanket. Her reddish hair was drifting in the water. She was weirdly beautiful as she looked straight at me with glimmering eyes. I could have sworn she was alive. She poked one arm out of a hole in the blanket and beckoned me near with a slow sweep of her arm. I went over to her and took her hand, but the fingers came off and mushed up in my grasp like a soaked hunk of Ivory soap. She looked sad about her hand and pulled her arm back inside the blanket."

Benjamin stopped then, wiping a hand across his face, and I saw amidst small liver spots that his hand had become moist with sweat. He cleared his throat, and for a moment I fretted that he might not tell me more, having already suppressed his emotions to the point of breaking.

"Then it seemed to me as though she was talking. The effort of speech caused one side of her perfect and perfectly white face to fall away from the skull. She commanded, 'Unbind the rope. Set me free.' Only then did I realize she was floating upright because one leg was tied to a concrete patio brick. I felt in my pockets and discovered I had my scaling knife with me. I bent down and sawed through the rope. As she floated upward and away from me, I heard her fading thoughts come back to me, offering a grateful sigh of thanks.

"At that moment I woke up in my boat, the morning sun warming my face. I was pretty well distressed about the dream. I tried to put it out of my mind as only a nightmare. Later that day, the Lady of Soap was found by a tourist. After that, I knew it was more than a dream. You'll not catch me on that lake again, nosireebob."

~~~~~

I finished up my research on the Soap Woman of Lake Crescent early in the afternoon at the newspaper morgue. There I saw a photo of Hallie Spraker Illingsworth. I was shocked by an uncanny resemblance, and the notice that she had worked in the Lake Crescent Lodge. I hurried back to the lodge and asked the bartender, "Is that auburn-haired waitress on duty tonight?"

"Who do you mean?" he asked.

"I talked to her yesterday while she was on her break. She didn't say her name."

"I'm afraid I don't know who you mean. There's no woman with auburn hair working here just now."

As he turned away to another customer, I sat at the bar nursing my Roy Rogers and pondering some of the things the nameless woman had said to me the day before. *She wants people to remember her.* I looked about the room. There was nothing unusual. Yet I could feel her presence, I was sure of it; there was a palpability in the shadows of the lodge—nothing frightening, but rather mocking, or even glad because the story was told.

Why the Loon Cries
A Legend of Mason Lake

SWOQUAD LIVED WITH his mother on the east side of the Olympic Peninsula along a salty shore at the edge of what is today called Hood Canal. Not far away from their home was a haunted lake. Swoquad was often told never to go there. "It is a place of evil spirits," his mother warned. "Someday, when you're old enough, you can go on a dream quest in that place and capture a spirit to make you strong. But now you are too small. The spirit would capture you."

"I'm not small!" he complained. "Don't I protect you every day?"

He was indeed a protective son, for his father was dead and he the man of the lodge. One day he ran into the lodge and found his mother weeping.

"Why are you weeping?" asked Swoquad.

"I'm not weeping," his mother said, pretending smoke from the firepit had stung her eyes. She turned away from her son to busy herself at something useless.

Swoquad knew that she was missing her husband, his father. Swoquad hardly remembered him. Nevertheless, he missed him too. He thought to himself, "I must become strong at once, or my mother will always cry, because she has no man to help her."

Three things were true of Swoquad. One thing was, he had a great love for his mother. The second thing was, he was surprisingly clever at convincing himself he needn't obey her much of the time. Last, he was a very good swimmer, as good as a seal or a porpoise.

That the lake was forbidden to him made it all the more attractive. One warm early summer day, Swoquad went to the shore of Mason Lake. He gazed left and right but saw no evidence of demons of any kind—not that he knew what to look for. He leapt into the clear waters and swam and dived and laughed the whole afternoon. He chased swift trout back and forth across the lake. One trout in particular seemed to be teasing him, as if it were aware that he had no net or spear. Swoquad swam after it like a dart. After many misses, he managed to grab the trout firmly. He tossed it ashore before it could wriggle out of his clutches, and it lay flopping amidst tall grass.

Famished from his long day of exercise, the boy kindled a fire on the shore, roasted his trout, and ate it noisily. The trout was the best he'd ever eaten, for in it lay an evil spirit teasing his senses. Once the demon was inside the boy, it did its dirty work. It transformed Swoquad into a black loon.

The terrified boy-loon flew home at once, calling over and over to his mother as he swooped around and around the lodge. He was frantic to tell her what had happened, but he could only make the sound of a loon. His mother came out of the lodge annoyed by the insistencies of the loon. She could not recognize her little boy, and snatched up a stick and slashed toward him as he flew near, for she disliked his discordant pleading.

Afraid he would be killed at any moment, the unhappy Swoquad flew back to the lake. He lives there yet, and still cries for his mother. To this day Swoquad can be heard repeating his plaintive notes, as a warning to other children as to the sorry fate of one who was disobedient.

Place of Thunder

A Legend of Snow Lake

§

ENUM-KLAH-PAH, "the place of thunder," is today called Snow Lake. This lake lies high in the Cascades between Tahoma (now called Mount Rainier) and Lake Keechelas. Many years ago, when first the firearm was introduced to Northwest peoples, a hunter named Bold Martin was riding his horse toward the Place of Thunder. All day long he had been led farther and farther afield by a stag so clever that Bold Martin was beginning to feel a personal enmity toward the beast. Now, this was a very bad frame of mind for a hunter, for a hunter must respect that which he kills. The wrong frame of mind can easily cause a hunter to succumb to evil powers.

Soon Bold Martin came to a rise and looked down the steep slope. He observed a large oval lake. All about the lake was open land. The rise upon which the hunter sat astride his horse was the highest point, and had only a scattering of timber at the ridge.

Lakes were rarely as lifeless in appearance as was this one. It struck the hunter as a bad place. He was a bit far off to see for certain, but it appeared to Bold Martin that along the nearest shore of the lake there were a number of white rocks. They were all about the size of two fists held together, and they were lined up in a row, evenly spaced, as though someone had put them there as a warning.

The hill was too steep to risk his pony's legs, so Bold Martin dismounted. The stag stopped halfway down the slope, its tail straight up. The hunter took aim with his musket. The hammer struck flint with a fine explosion. Blood spewed from the rump of the stag where the musketball entered. The animal stumbled, but regained its feet almost at once and continued toward the lake.

As Bold Martin reloaded, he thought, "That was a good hit. I'm surprised that stag can still run. He'll fall down in a minute." He put a ball into the musket and was ready for another shot should it prove necessary. The stag was too far away, however, so the hunter hung his musket on his back and started downward toward the lake. It was steep enough in places that he had to descend backward, clinging to the slope.

He hoped he wouldn't have to use another musket ball. The stag should drop in a moment or two from loss of blood. Then Bold Martin could rush upon it and slit its throat with a knife.

Distant, distant thunder murmured solemnly, like a waterfall far up in heaven. A few large flakes of snow were falling out the sky, dancing in the rising breeze like butterflies turned to ice. Bold Martin stood on a small rocky protrusion halfway down the slope to observe the wounded animal. Odd that it no longer limped. Perhaps his shot hadn't been as good as he thought. The light snow created an illusion. The stag seemed to have turned ghostly white.

Loosened gravel skittered down the slope. One larger rock went tumbling and made a loud crack when it hit another rock at the base of the hill. At that moment, the pure white rocks along the edge of the lake turned up on their sides. Bold Martin thought they weren't rocks after all, but huge freshwater clams. Yet how could it be that one by one they each rolled into the lake? Bold Martin gasped at the weird sight. He convinced himself his eyes had been mistaken. They weren't clams or even rocks, but clods of snow the wind had picked up and blown into the lake.

A mist had gathered over the water. This mist appeared to coagulate into a faint form, like a giant. That giant began to stride atop the water toward the stag, if not toward Bold Martin himself! For a moment Bold Martin's heart caught in his throat; he wondered if he oughtn't scramble up the slope, regain his horse, and speed away. But the wind quickly dispersed the illusion of a giant. Bold Martin laughed at himself. In such an eerie place, a trick of snow and mist easily played on his imagination.

Thunder rumbled anew, sounding closer, as though a divinity were pounding on the mother of drums. Was it an omen? Bold Martin began to feel certain the place was truly haunted. Yes, he should go back up the hill at once! He would have done so, but a good hunter never abandons a wounded animal. It would be cruel as well as a waste of good meat. So he loped and slid on down the hill, managing to stay on both feet.

~~~~~

The beast was headed straight for the lake. As every moment passed, it looked paler and paler amidst the mist and snowflakes. If it swam to the other side, Bold Martin might have a devil of a time tracking it afoot, having first to circle the lake and then trail it until it dropped from its wound. Hoping to forestall this, he shouldered the musket, took careful aim, and released the hammer. In the same moment, the heavens flashed silently, one enormous strobe of light spanning the horizon. Then with the musket's explosion, the ball shot forth and caught the stag high in the shoulder. Scant moments later, a deafening thunder shook the ground and vibrated the very heart of Bold Martin.

The stag stopped in its tracks. It *was* white! Even its antlers were white. The stag was as white as the snow around it, though Bold Martin was certain that yesterday, when he had begun to track it, it had not been white. A red stream gouted from the shoulder, marring the stag's otherwise perfect and nearly incandescent whiteness. Even the blood grew paler as it flowed from the wound; that which spattered the ground had no color.

The beast turned more than halfway around to gaze at Bold Martin. Its eyes were tragic and intelligent. The hunter always pitied his prey, but never before had he felt such a pang of regret. Then the stag turned slowly away and looked into the water, as though searching for something that was in the lake. It stood stone-still; for a moment Bold Martin thought it had died standing. He ran forward, his spent musket across his back and knife in hand.

Then the white stag leapt headfirst into the lake and vanished under the water. Bold Martin ceased running and watched for the swimming stag—or its corpse—to surface. It never did. Thunder now roared around him over and over. Strobes of distant lightning seemed brighter and brighter as dusk descended—a dusk made white by mist and snow.

~~~~~

Bold Martin turned from the frightful lake and headed toward the hillside. Flurries of snow were now so thick around him he could not see the skimpy timbers on the ridge. The dropping temperature gripped him as if it were the icy waters themselves. He started up the slope, scrambling on hands and knees. He knew he must find shelter or die. A mixture of rain and snow made the ground slick to grasp. Over and over he slipped back, then climbed anew. Halfway up, with cold wet snow blinding and stinging his eyes, he gasped for need of breath, and felt as if he were truly in the lake. He threw himself on the protruding rock at the halfway point, panting, and gazed back at the lake half expecting to see his own pale body floating there. He saw snow swirling and dancing about the surface of the waters like smoke from a fire, funneling upward and then bending toward him like the claws of a giant bird. When the funnel reached him, it was filled with sharp knives of sleet that cut his face and hands.

Bold Martin struggled upward until he reached the summit. The wind was now so terrible he had to remove his belt and lash himself to a tree. The trees bent low in the wind. He saw his pony with its head facing downward, its forehead against a tree. "I will die here," said Bold Martin, and was surprised to find that his greatest worry was that his pony would not find its way home.

But soon the wind died down. So cold he was numb, Bold Martin regained his horse and rode carefully through the night until he arrived at a camp where other hunters were waiting out the storm. He collapsed in the leaning shelter they had built, and could speak to no one until the following day, which was so clear and bright you would never have guessed there had been such a storm.

~~~~~

Most of Bold Martin's fellow hunters did not believe the story about the deer entering the lake, though Bold Martin's seriousness gave them pause to wonder. There were two older hunters who credited his tale. These were Early Star and Old Man Who Shoots Straight. Early Star said, "There are tahmahnawis spirits dwelling in that lake, very dangerous. If a warrior could capture one of those spirits, he would become indestructible, and no one would dare challenge him."

Old Man Who Shoots Straight added, "When I was a young man,

I was called Far Rider, and Early Star was my usual companion even then. We hunted together in that very place."

"That's right, we did, but only once," said Early Star.

Shoots Straight continued, "We came from the low side, and saw across the lake to the ridge. On the ridge was a family of white mountain goats. The goats pranced about and fought with one another, butting heads in play. They climbed a tall rock. Early Star and I circled, one to the left, the other to the right, heading around the lake so that we would come upon the goats from both directions. We had made boasts to one another about who would kill one first, and I was eager to win the boast. With bows and arrows, we had to get fairly close to the high rock. When I shot one, it was a big ram. The arrow went deep; I was sure it went into the heart. The ram fell from the rock and landed near Place of Thunder Lake."

"I'll never forget," said Early Star. "At first I was disappointed to have lost my boast. It was strange and impossible, but the ram suddenly stood up. I was thinking that though I didn't win, Far Rider hadn't entirely won either! The ram looked into the lake, standing perfectly still. As I was nearest, I started toward him to finish him off with my knife, so that I could claim half the first kill as mine. But the ram leapt into the water headfirst! He never came up again. At that very moment, a terrible storm came upon us as from nowhere, and we barely made it back alive."

Shoots Straight said, "That is why none of us ever returned to hunt in that place. So believe Bold Martin, and remember what we have said, for we have many seasons of experience above you, and we know such things are true."

The Vanished Great Lake

A Legend of the First People of Spokane Falls

)))

SOME WHILE AFTER the end of the glacier age, much of the region that is now Eastern Washington became a green paradise. The Great Spokane Lake ran eastward from the area of today's city for many days' journeying afoot. The lake was created in the days of the Great Flood, when first the ice withdrew, and was continuously renewed by the still-melting ice of winter's faded rule. The waters were pure and sweet, for having been held in stasis since the beginning of time, it was water as originally created.

Upon the lake were many wonderful big islands. There were pleasant peoples living thereon who caught trout and collected berries in the warm sun. The name Spokane, "The Sun People," dates to those prehistoric times. On the outer shores of the lake were many villages sprinkled about. Beyond the villages were woodlands rich in game. No clan felt competitive in this world of plenitude, and each clan was friendly with all others.

As these people were so fortunate, among them the arts flourished; they were singers, poets, dancers, prophets, weavers, and painters. They were petroglyph people, and their mysterious works of art, painted or carved on cliffs and rock walls, are all that remains to remind us of their aesthetic impulses.

As the lake was shallow, it was unheard of that anyone drowned there; and because the sun warmed it greatly, even though the water ran from off the cold ice in the north, children had daily swimming contests. Even the elderly were strong swimmers. Had the lake remained forever, the people would surely have become an aquatic race, mermaids and mermen, never wishing to leave the comfort of their pleasing liquid realm.

~~~~~

On a fine spring day, with wildflowers bursting upon all the wooded shores and islands, a young man called Watches The Sky Within Him reposed amidst yellow poppies. Inexplicably, for the first time in a joyous life devoid of deprivations and sorrows, terrible thoughts sprang upon him. These thoughts were in the nature of a vision.

Never before had he envisioned anything so worrisome. Therefore he knew not whether to believe such unexpectedly evil ruminations. He said to himself, without wanting to say it, "All this loveliness will be swept away. The ice of winter's long rule has departed from this country. Soon even the water flowing from the glacier's lingering presence in the north will vanish. Many of the people will perish and this Country of the Great Lake will be a desert."

At first he thought himself mad to have imagined such a thing. Somehow the sun had rattled him. Then his eyes filled with moisture, for he well knew that this sorry prophesy was as apt to be true as were his former visions. He said to himself, "Four times I have had visions of beautiful occurrences that came to pass within two or three moons. This fifth imagining is so unlike the others. Yet horribleness has seeped into my mind in much the same way as formerly beautifulness has done. Woe awaits the world! Even so, do I not perceive a final outcome that is in the nature of a consolation? But what shall be called 'final'? Shall I live to know what the consolation is to be? This I know not."

Picking up his fishing spear and the string of fish he had caught with such ease, he returned to his island village at the mouth of a murmuring stream. He told his mother and father his sorry prophesy. They were gloomy to hear it. But people who have been wonderfully privileged by the Sky Spirit and the Earth Spirit have difficulty fully grasping the very idea of catastrophe.

The family of Watching The Sky Within Him called into their tent of woven grass mats a woman who was chief of the village. Seldom had anyone so young risen to her status. For all her lack of many winters, she was noted for fairness and consideration. She was very beautiful as well, with shimmering black hair, a lilting sweet voice, and a nose like a little hawk, from which she gained her name, Chief Little Hawk.

When she heard the prophesy, she sent the young prophet to assist an elderly wiseman along the village path, so the elder could lend his wisdom to their impromptu council. Together they considered the prophesy of Watches The Sky Within Him. All his previous prophesies, they admitted, had been so thrillingly pleasant that the people had accepted them with gladness in their hearts, and had been rewarded for having done so. It was difficult to dismiss this unglad vision out of hand, though they wished they could do so.

They spoke, and sang prayers requesting guidance, and spoke again, until late in the evening. The young prophet's mother prepared a fine meal that lent a festive air to so unfestive an occasion. The moon-boat sailed along the Milky Way in a sky salted by the campfires of heaven. In all the world, so far as could be gauged, there was only pleasantness, warmth, and beauty.

At last the wiseman came to a conclusion on the subject. He had

The Vanished Great Lake

eaten a fine trout roasted in herb leaves and not found a single bone in it, so well had it been prepared for his gums. This resulted in a happy frame of mind. He said, "My stomach tells me there can be no pain, that even though I am old and must in good time die, I will do so surrounded by loving hands. I will go away smiling to sit by the campfires of the sky. What our young prophet has seen must be regarded as the true end of all things. But that end is a far distance from now."

Chief Little Hawk gazed from the old wiseman to the young prophet. She could see that even Watches The Sky Within Him wanted to believe the venerable's opinion. She sighed a deep sigh and with one hand raised for silence, spoke with a tinge of sadness. "Whether the end comes soon or long seasons from today, what can we do to change it? There is nothing we can do. What then can we be, except blithe?"

With this weak reassurance, the woman chief stood, assisted the venerable, and led him away from the hut of Watches The Sky Within Him and his parents.

~~~~~

It came about just so. Upon a summer morning only three moons after the prophesy, all the villages about the lake and upon the islands were awakened by a frightful rumbling. The waters of the lake were leaping upward in the manner of a stormy sea. In scant moments, the mat houses were swept away by high, pounding waters, and with their houses went all the wealth of the people. The islanders discovered their islands sinking away or breaking into pieces. They leapt into canoes and struggled toward the distant shore. Many a boat was overturned in the waves. As people floundered in the waters, some were able to survive the roiling shallows and make it ashore. Yet a greater number were lost.

Watches The Sky Within Him treaded water swiftly, trying to

grasp his mother and father without himself sinking. His mother slapped him sternly and pushed herself away, screaming wildly for her son to save his father, saying, "You cannot swim and hold us both!" His mother was lost in that instant. The young prophet wept sorely as he clung to his father and tried to reach the shore. But now his father struggled against Watches The Sky Within Him. He cried out to his wife, "Why did you sacrifice yourself? Can I live without you?" He dropped away like a stone to find her.

His father's last words echoed in the mind of Watches The Sky Within Him. He said to himself, "I cannot live without them." He ceased to struggle in order to drown. But the firm young hand of Chief Little Hawk snatched at the collar of his shirt. She cried out amidst the storming waves, "I have lost our old wiseman! I will not lose you! Come, we will swim together, or we both die!"

The waters pitched at them as they came ashore, as though loath to leave them with their lives. Together the prophet and the woman chief joined in the headlong rush of refugees from the murderous lake.

To add to the horrors, the sun was inexplicably engulfed in blackness. There was something evil and unnatural in the clouds. As the people fled to the hills hoping for safety, a choking ash began to fall from the darkened sky. Many collapsed, unable to breathe. The woman chief and the prophet found scraps of grass matting to press over their faces as they pushed toward higher ground. On a ridge they took shelter in a shallow cavern crowded with other panic-stricken survivors.

For five days the earth shook. For five weeks ash and rain fell out of the sky. The ash was so thick that it was difficult to tell day from night. For five months there was no game in the countryside, no berries growing in the woods. The forests died. The water, fouled with ash, contained only dead and rotting fish.

The Vanished Great Lake

The lake began to recede rapidly, seeping away into the earth, so the exposed lake bottom became cracked clay. People prayed day and night. A few eked out a bare survival on roots. The sorriest of the refugees skinned the bark from fallen trees, boiled it, and used it as food.

The prophet managed occasionally to kill a bird passing over the blasted realm. He shared his feeble meals with Chief Little Hawk. The remnants of a once-numerous people gathered around the young chief, who alone of all their royalty had not perished.

One day Chief Little Hawk gathered them in one place. She said, "Our prophet knew the catastrophe was coming. But what could we do to prepare? There was nothing, so we have come to this sad state. What then is the use of prophesy? Every prophesy has its purpose. Watches The Sky Within Him envisioned a consolation for all of us. Come! He and I will lead you to a good place."

They travelled afoot, for these people had no horses in those days. They were a pitiful lot, wetting one another's shoulders with their tears. But the prophesy was true. They followed a sluggish rill that was all that remained of the great lake. As they proceeded, the rill widened and became a river. This river had no fish in it until they reached a waterfall. In the bay below the falls, salmon frolicked, leaping head over tail.

Here the people settled and prospered for eight thousand years. The descendant of Watches The Sky Within Him and Chief Little Hawk was Whistelpossum, the famous chief of the three Spokane tribes, a man possessed of all the vigor of his ancestress and all the veracity of his ancestor, and to whom this story belonged.

You may today visit the pooling waters north of Bridge Avenue between Post and Monroe Streets in the city of Spokane. There you will see where a prosperous people swam gaily amidst the salmon.

Bone-Cleaner of Blue Lake

A Legend of the Moses Coulee

IN THE MOSES Coulee (began the Sanpoil Indian cowboy) is a large lake, Lake Nuquispum, with an island in the middle. The lake is south of Sanpoil territory near the Columbia River. The whites call it Blue Lake becausee of its color. It's a nice-looking lake, but appearances can fool people. Though it has a lot of perch and sunfish in it, no one likes to fish there. The lake has a bad reputation. A bone-cleaner lives in it. No one knows what the bone-cleaner looks like, but there was a time when a lot of strange animals lived in various lakes in the Old Coulee. You still encounter the petrified bones of those monsters from time to time. The bone-cleaner must be one of those creatures, still lingering from the long-ago days.

That bone-cleaner has a herd of cattle that come up every day from the bottom of the lake and graze the hills. If anyone tries to get near that herd, they run swiftly back into the lake without making a ripple. One day not long ago Ralph Lucky Star said, "I'm going to that lake and catch me a spirit." He wasn't such a lucky guy, but people called him lucky because with all the trouble he had gotten himself into, he was lucky just to have stayed alive.

Ralph always tempted fate. He went with some friends, including Billy Curlew of the Moses-Columbia band, to Blue Lake. Ralph said,

"I'm good with a rifle, admit it."

"Yes, yes," said Billy.

Ralph took aim and shot one of the cows. It fell right down as the rest of the herd ran into the lake and disappeared. Ralph and his buddies went to where the cow fell, but saw only a puddle of water.

"Well!" said Ralph. "I'm a strong swimmer, admit it."

"Yes, yes."

So he leapt in Blue Lake and started to swim toward the island. When he was halfway to the island, he gave one sharp little yelp and went down like a rock. His friends waited to see what would happen. Ralph Lucky Star didn't reappear. Billy Curlew said, "Well, that's the end of him!"

Two weeks later, Ralph's skeleton was found on the shore of the lake, laid out neatly on the opposite side from where he went down. Those bones were clean and white, without a trace of flesh. His flesh hadn't rotted away, for two weeks isn't long enough for that to happen. No, his flesh had been cleaned off by something that ate it— the bone-cleaner. The Sanpoils never go there as a result. It was unlucky for Ralph Lucky Star. Maybe a smarter guy than Ralph could find a way to reach that island safely, but it won't be me who tries.

Young Man Who Became Weary
A Legend of Willapa Bay

}}}

THERE WAS A chief's son of a village situated on a small peninsula in Willapa Bay. This young man's name was Yakhan, "His Son." His best friend was Yakiyal, "Commoner." They did everything together and loved each other very much. Yakhan never postured in any way that would suggest he thought himself more important than his lowborn companion. He took no advantage of his birth to lord over others.

Together he and Yakiyal set out in the morning to visit a nearby village. They met Ahatau, "A Maiden," the daughter of her people's chief. Because Yakiyal was extremely beautiful, the chief's daughter liked him at once. She did not care that he was a commoner. Ahatau had a slave girl named Agaylaitish, "Her Maid." Yakhan noticed the slave girl, who he immediately found wonderfully attractive, with a combination of shyness and boldness that fascinated Yakhan.

The two young men went often to the other village. It became known that a chief's daughter loved a commoner. Ahatau took some teasing from her sisters and cousins, but secretly everyone approved of her choice, for Yakiyal was the comeliest man imaginable. His father had few claims of birth, but he was wealthy in his own right, and there was every expectation that Ahatau's father would receive a big marriage price.

Not so for Yakhan and Agaylaitish. When it became known that Yakhan was enamored of a slave girl, his father was mortified and became abusive. Every morning, before his son set out, the chief berated Yakhan in no uncertain terms. When Yakhan said, "Will you at least meet with Agaylaitish, father? You don't know what she was before she became a slave," his mother joined in and scolded him for speaking to his father in such a disobedient manner.

The chief of the other village would not set Agaylaitish free for fear of bad feelings with Yakhan's father, who was mighty. Finally, Yakhan was unable to see Agaylaitish at all, for she was sent someplace, and no one would tell him where.

He asked everyone. They said, "She went away." He was distressed over her disappearance, yet no one would ease his mind about her. Then one day Yakhan and Yakiyal went to a wild marsh north along the bay, near the Willapa River, to be apart from other people. In this place there were only birds, hundreds of birds singing and nesting in the trees, and mother ducks hidden in shore-grass. Though it was a beautiful place of solitude, Yakhan sighed as if weighted with thoughts. He said, "I am weary, Yakiyal, weary."

Yakiyal replied, "Since you cannot have your choice of bride, neither will I ever marry."

"No, no, you must marry Princess Ahatau. You are fortunate and must not turn your back on fortune. As for me, I will go away."

"If you go, I will be unhappy," said Yakiyal, "for I love you greatly."

"No, no, I am weary."

In the afternoon Yakhan went home and lay down in his father's lodge. He ate nothing. He rose early and ventured with his friend into the woods by the marshland. They selected the high dead limb of a lightning-blasted tree and used it for their arrows' target. Yakiyal made a perfect hit. So did Yakhan. Yakiyal whooped in praise for himself and his friend, but Yakhan was unresponsive. He said, "Oh, my heart is weary, weary. If you love me, you will see me always, but I must go."

"No, Yakhan, no! Don't leave me, for I would be unhappy."

That evening, Yakhan again lay down in the lodge without eating. So it was for five days. He shot targets with his friend, he moaned about his sorrows, and he went home and slept without eating. After the five days, he and Yakiyal took off all their clothing and went swimming in the bay. Yakhan dived under the water five times. Each time he resurfaced, his friend became increasingly fearful that Yakhan would not come back to land, but was purposely drowning himself.

The fifth time Yakiyal saw Yakhan, he was a long way from shore, far out in the shallow bay, lying upon a snag. Yakiyal perceived that his friend was changed in some spiritual manner and might choose to stay in the sea forever.

Yakiyal cried and cried. He sat on the shore crying. Yakhan looked at him from the snag and said, "Why cry for me, Yakiyal? This is the way we shall do it. If you love me, you will always see me. Come to this place and we shall shoot targets. Tell no one! But if you cease to love me, then you may tell where I am. Come to me tomorrow and we will enjoy the day." Then the chief's son dove into the sea and was gone.

~~~~~

Yakiyal cried on his way home. He told no one what had happened to Yakhan. The next day he went to the shore nearest the snag and Yakhan came out of the water. They shot targets; it was like always. "You told no one?" asked Yakhan. "No one," said Yakiyal.

That evening someone asked Yakiyal, "Where is Yakhan?" Yakiyal replied, "I have not seen him in a while." The chief said, "Someone must have killed my son." He sent the villagers into the surrounding

Young Man Who Became Weary

woods to look for his son. The search extended to neighboring villages. There was no sign of Yakhan. Every morning, Yakiyal went out alone to wander along Willapa Bay toward the marsh. He would stand near the shore until his friend came out. Yakhan would say, "Never tell them; if you do, you will see me no more."

People began to wonder about Yakiyal's behavior. The chief said, "That commoner has killed my son and hidden his body. Why else is he so secretive?"

Five mornings Yakiyal went out to the marsh alone, eating nothing this whole while. One day the chief's slaves followed him and saw Yakhan and Yakiyal shooting targets. Yakhan's father's slaves reported, "Your son is well. We saw him shooting targets with Yakiyal."

When Yakiyal came back into the village that evening, he was dragged before the chief who said, "Why have you been keeping his whereabouts a secret?" But Yakiyal said nothing. He made no excuse. The chief let him go, but the next morning, the slaves again followed him without making a sound.

"There are people watching us secretly," said Yakhan. "I fear you have told them."

"I didn't. Your father asked and asked. I said nothing."

"Tell my father, 'When I was in your lodge, you were ashamed of me, for I would not distinguish blood from blood. Why complain if I am gone? Let me be, you who are ashamed.'"

In the evening, Yakiyal went home, and Yakhan went into the water. Yakiyal took the message to the chief, who gripped a spear's haft until his knuckles were white, but restrained himself from striking the messenger. He commanded, "Tell me at least why you will not reveal his whereabouts?"

"You scolded him every day because of his love for the slave

Agaylaitish. You shamed him and it hurt his heart. You made him weary, as now I am weary, and I begin to understand him. He has changed his nature and does not live on the land. You can see him never again."

Yakhan's father felt guilt and sorrow, but more than that, his pride was injured. Several of the relatives mourned. They said to the chief, "Buy him the slave of that chief's daughter; then he'll come back." The chief replied, "I don't know where she went. Yet if I can find her, I will buy her for my son, at any cost."

The next morning, Yakiyal set out and stood by the sea. Yakhan appeared on the snag, and then swam ashore. Yakiyal said, "They are willing to buy Agaylaitish for you. You cannot marry her, but she will be your slave. You can treat her as you would a wife."

Yakhan said, "Tell them for me, 'Keep still! You are still ashamed of me.'"

In the evening, Yakiyal was taken before the chief, who demanded, "What did he say?"

"'Be still, you are still ashamed.'"

Unbeknownst to Yakiyal, when he left the next morning for the marsh, all the youths in the village met with the chief. They received his orders and made themselves ready for a hunt.

In the woods by the marsh, Yakhan said to Yakiyal, "We are surrounded. Run, or they will kill you." The two friends separated and young hunters surrounded Yakhan. They tried to close in on him, but he pushed right through them. He had become exceedingly strong. They saw him dive into the bay. He emerged and lay on the snag. The hunters went back to the village in tears of defeat. Then the seasoned warriors came forth. The chief said, "As he has become a monster, we will treat him like a monster! Let us kill my son!"

Yakiyal visited the shore in the place where the chief's son usually appeared. He waited and waited, but Yakhan did not come forth. Yakiyal began to cry, certain he had seen his friend for the last time. Then he looked up, and Yakhan was standing there. Yakiyal said, "Oh, my friend! I was so unhappy! I thought you had left me forever."

"I shall tell you when they have made me weary," replied Yakhan. "Until then, you need not cry. Tell them, 'Leave me alone.' If they will do so, then you and I may continue as before." Then Yakhan looked quickly about. He said, "Well! Here they come!"

Across the bay, fishermen were coming in three lines of canoes, each with a long net in the water. They had tied large stones to the nets so that the nets hung down. They surrounded Yakhan's route of escape. Then warriors came forth from the woods with their arrows ready. They shot Yakhan full of arrows. He leapt into the bay and disappeared. The nets did not shake. All the arrows came to the surface and floated.

That evening, Yakiyal said to the chief and to the warriors and to the young hunters and the slaves, "Can you not leave Yakhan be? If you bother him further, none of us will see him again. Why won't you be satisfied to allow us to shoot targets in the marsh?"

The next morning he sat by the bay and once again he wept. He gave forth loud wails of weeping, for he felt abandoned and alone. Yakhan came out of the water and said, "Oh, my poor friend, do you still love me so? My heart is weary, weary. Look there, once again they are surrounding us. Once more they will shoot me full of arrows. Look, they have brought harpoons and spears, hoping to do me harm. Oh, I am weary, weary."

The canoes came in five rows. The marksmen leapt out of the woods. Spears and harpoons and arrows struck Yakhan's body front and back. He ran as though unweakened toward the water, all those shafts sticking out of him. Several young hunters who were swift afoot leapt forth and grabbed him, but he threw them off with ease. They tumbled shouting. As Yakhan dove into the water, the fishermen threw more spears. They tried to hold him with nets, but he passed through the nets without shaking them. Then the harpoons, spears, and arrows floated on the water. Yakhan emerged on his favorite snag far from shore.

On the shore, Yakiyal was grabbing bows from warriors and throwing them on the ground. He shouted, "Weep! Weep! Now he will go away, for he is weary! No one will ever see him again! He is dead to his family, dead to this world, dead to all of us!"

Already the women and the children in the village were lamenting with loud wails. They surrounded Yakhan's mother, who had not approved of her husband's desire to kill their wayward and transformed son. When the warriors and hunters straggled home, they listened to their wives, their sisters, their daughters. Then, in shame and sadness, the warriors cut off their hair. Yakiyal walked amidst the people, crying all the while. For five days the village mourned with Yakiyal, who embraced Yakhan's mother.

On the fifth day, Yakiyal returned to the usual meeting place. He saw Yakhan on the snag. Yakhan did not come ashore, but spoke from the snag. "Weep no more for me, Yakiyal, for truly I am not dead, I am living. You are always crying for me, but listen, I have a nice house much like yours, in a place where there are no commoners, and no chiefs, and no slaves. Agaylaitish has come there, for my father secretly tried to have her killed, and that is why she went away. I have taken a new name, Emogoalekc, the spirit-protector. Now stop crying, for the one who loves me will become chief of the people."

Young Man Who Became Weary

And it was so. Yakiyal the commoner's son became a chief, and his wife, the mother of the tribe, was Princess Ahatau. Yakiyal always said his good fortune was due to Emogoalekc, the sea-prince, protector of the downtrodden, the giver of strength to hunters and fishermen, and to this day the powerful spirit of the Shoalwater tribe.

The Swan Queen and the Elk Child
A Legend of Horsethief Lake

〿

THERE LIVED UPON Horsethief Lake, near the Columbia River in the southern part of the Klickitat nation, a gigantic swan called Hawilakok. This Swan Queen required solitude and commanded quietude. She hated for a lot people to visit her lake at one time. So long as her needs were respected, she was willing to share all the bounty of her tranquil home: the edible roots; the tough grasses that grew in the shallows such as were useful in weaving mats and baskets; the many kinds of fish that dwelt amidst the calm, pleasing waters; the geese and game that lingered upon and around the expansive lake . . .

However, if someone visiting the lake became noisy, this aroused Hawilakok's anger. She would fluff out her wings, push out the feathers at her chest until her considerable size was nearly doubled, and stamp her webbed feet upon the waters until the waves became exceedingly dangerous, spreading to all corners of that sizable lake. At such times, a fisherman, a swimmer, or even a hunter wandering near the shore would have to be quick to escape drowning.

The Swan Queen's lake became the preferred place to send young men and women when they reached the proper age for a dream-quest, so that they could find a spirit-protector to guide them all their lives. Not all such quests worked out for the better. They were true trials, and the trailside was littered with the bones of those who failed.

~~~~~

Once a young woman, upon reaching puberty, was sent away from her village for the sake of her first menstruation, the time when a girl was expected to receive a protective spirit. This young woman had been so spoiled throughout her childhood that she sought her spirit not as a test of merit, but as her due.

She said to herself, "I will go to Horsethief Lake and find my spirit-protector. That's the place to obtain an especially strong one. Then I'll have a lot of power and can become a medicine woman or do whatever I wish. If I fast many days and exert myself by swimming in that lake, Hawilakok will reward me with long life and plenty of riches. I'll marry well and possess slaves and never have to do any work. Am I not as beautiful as Hawilakok? Is she not a fine-looking woman of her kind, as I am of mine? I need not fear Hawilakok's wrath, for how could she do other than recognize and admire my qualities! Yes, I'll go there at once."

As she explored the forest and made her way toward the lake, the young woman continued to think vaingloriously of her own excellence and the promising future, hers for the taking. By such thinking, she was preparing her heart in entirely the wrong manner.

When she arrived at the lake, she had already fasted five days. She congratulated herself for having done so. She leapt amidst the tule rushes and splashed her way to deeper water, crying out for joy. Had anyone seen her antics or heard her commotion, she might have been warned, "The Swan Queen doesn't like so much racket." As the young woman gazed about the lake, she could not help but believe that all this beauty had been planned and laid out entirely for her own approval, benefit, and enjoyment.

The maiden dove under the water and held her breath a long while. She swam through a school of baby catfishes, whose tiny whiskers brushed against her coppery skin. She swept her arms, frightening them, dispersing them in all directions. Bubbles escaped her lungs as she laughed beneath the waves.

When at last she raised her head to gulp the air, she threw back her long hair with an arc of spray, opened her eyes, and to her amazement saw before her the enormous Swan Queen. The long neck was like the body of a sea serpent arching into heaven. The swan's head was cocked to one side, and a huge yellow eye looked at the noisy swimmer with acute malignancy.

Of a sudden, the maiden realized her errors. She began to swim away as rapidly as she could, heading for the tule rushes. The swan followed at a leisurely pace, as though herding her out of the lake, forcing her to go one way and not another. As the maiden neared the shore, she saw the brown branches of a dead tree sticking up amidst the tule. Into these branches she climbed, only to discover that she was in the antlers of an enormous elk buck! The buck immediately lifted his head and gave out a trumpeting sound, as though speaking to the Swan Queen. The Swan Queen snapped her bill in a series of clicks, bobbing her head up and down, replying to the elk's speech.

Then the elk splashed out of the shallows of Horsethief Lake and ran toward the mountains.

"Let me down!" cried the maiden, clinging to the antlers lest she fall and be killed.

"Why should I let you down?" the running elk replied. "The Swan Queen said I could have you for my wife."

"Why would I want to be the wife of an elk? Can you not see I am

The Swan Queen and the Elk Child

too beautiful to be given to an animal! I must marry the son of a chief and nothing less!"

"I am the son of the Elk Chief," said the elk.

"I don't care!" said the maiden. "I want down!"

But the elk would neither let her down nor slow his headlong pace enough for her to dare to leap from the perch. She resorted to a subterfuge and said, "Oh! I'm so thirsty! Stop by a stream so I can get water!"

"Look in my left ear, and you will find water," said the elk.

It was such a curious idea, she simply had to take a look, and sure enough, his ear was full of pure bright sparkling water. At her desire, the water issued forth like a rivulet. She caught it in the cup of her hand. Then she said, "I have fasted for five days! I must have something to eat at once! Stop by that field of huckleberry bushes!"

"Look in my right ear and you will find all kinds of berries."

She looked in his ear, and sure enough, it was like a basket of sweet ripe salmonberries, black-cap berries, huckleberries, and many similar succulent fruits. She ate several, as it was true that she'd been famished.

"As you can see," said the elk, "I am perfectly capable of providing for a wife."

"All the same," she said, "I don't see that I would like to be your wife."

"Very well. You decide, but first you must meet my brothers."

As the elk hurried along, the maiden grasped at the limbs of trees. She hoped to make her escape, but the first few branches she got hold of came loose in her hand.

"What are you up to?" asked the elk.

"I'm not talking to you," she replied.

She wedged the captured branches in the buck's antlers. Then she climbed to the highest point of one antler and leapt upward into a cedar tree.

It took a few moments to regain her breath, for she was winded by the blow of the limb she had landed against. She hung with the branch under her armpits pressed against her small breasts. Then, climbing down from the tree, she began to run in the direction of her village, which was now quite far. She stopped only once, to squat down and urinate at the side of the trail.

~~~~~

The elk peeled his eyes as far back as he could, but he could not really see the top of his head. "What are you doing now?" he asked, but the young woman didn't speak to him. He saw the edge of one of the branches she'd wedged in his antlers. He thought it was the maiden's foot. Satisfied that she was still in his antlers, he ran up the mountainside and came to an elk band.

"Brothers!" he cried out. "I have caught a human wife!"

"Where is she?" the eldest elk inquired.

"In my antlers!"

"You have only twigs and fir boughs in your antlers."

"What! The Swan Queen said I could have the maiden. Has she divorced me so soon? I shall follow after her and beg her to come home."

So saying, the elk turned back to seek his wife. He came to the cedar tree into which she had leapt, and smelled that she had been there. He rubbed his fur against the bark to mingle his scent with hers before continuing on his way. Next he came to the place where she had squatted down. He urinated in the same place. By this means he worked a virile magic upon her.

The Swan Queen and the Elk Child

He sought her the rest of the day, until he discovered that his wife had returned to her village near The Dalles, where there were hunters who kill elk. He returned to his band in sad dejection.

~~~~~

Within a few weeks, the maiden realized she was with child. She tried to hide her pregnancy from her family. Before her stomach had grown so big that people noticed, she went to live in the forest near Horsethief Lake. She complained to Hawilakok, "You are responsible for this, Queen of Swans! Very well, I accept you as my guardian, and the guardian of my child! But don't expect any favors from me, for I am unmarried, and this pregnancy is not good for me."

She never actually saw the Swan Queen again, yet Hawilakok often heard the young woman's berating opinions. Then the elk child was born with little bud-horns on his forehead and round dark eyes. The young mother bound the child to a cradle and put a board over the horns so no one would see them. In those days, all the people in that part of the country were flatheads. Because her people compressed the foreheads of their infants while the the infants were strapped to cradleboards, it incited no curiosity when the young mother hid the hornbuds in this manner.

Her grandmother saw her returning to the village with a cradleboard on her back. The grandmother said, "Here comes my wayward granddaughter, and she has a child! Well! Children are nice; we'll make the best of things."

The young mother said, "Grandmother, I have a child now. Listen to me carefully. Under no circumstance must you remove him from the cradleboard. On the contrary, he must remain on the board, with his head compressed, at all times."

In the days that followed, no matter what she did, the young mother kept the child bound to the cradleboard. She often left the child propped up in a corner of the house and neglected him. The grandmother said, "You should nurse your son now, he cries for milk."

"When I'm ready," she replied.

"You should loosen him from the cradle so he can learn to crawl."

"No, no, I'll do as I please."

One day when the mother was out gathering food or wood, the grandmother listened to the child crying and crying. She felt so sorry for him that finally she unbound him from the cradle. Immediately he leapt to his feet. With a little mewling elk-calf sound he ran out of the house. As he ran through the village, he turned into a little elk, bawling and kicking his hoofs. He fled in the direction of Horsethief Lake.

When the mother returned with a basket of roots, she learned her child had turned into an elk and run away. Then she admitted it was the child of an elk. Though she had mistreated the child, she was not heartless. She grieved for her loss. She would accept no blame, however, but said, "That elk and that old swan Hawilakok did my son no good!"

Though Horsethief Lake was far off, the woman's disparaging proclamation reached Hawilakok. The elk-child came to the lake and rejoined his father and the rest of the elk band. Hawilakok said to the elk band, "A protective spirit was granted to that woman, and look how little she has achieved! Had she cherished this elk boy, there would have been elk in this region for all time. But now I will tell you of a pleasant land far north of here, so that you need never again come to this place."

Hawilakok thereafter withheld her wealth from people. Geese no longer nested by the lake. The catfish disappeared, and fishing was poor in that lake for many generations. Even the grass with which women wove their mats and baskets became thin, brittle, and scarce.

You will see Hawilakok at Horsethief Lake if you go there, especially in autumn. If you are very still, she appears as a mist upon the water, wherein all sounds are muffled and morning light suffused, and the only thing you will hear is the soft rustling of her wings.

The Changelings

A Wapato Lake Legend

A STRANGE CREATURE called the Huluk used to live in Lake Tualatin, now called Wapato Lake, a quiet shallow lake surrounded by gorgeous greenery. The Huluk is not there now, because it outgrew the lake and went to live elsewhere. Today no one sees it; long ago, it was often seen. This story happened in bygone days, when the Huluk still dwelt in that lake.

By nature sluggish, the Huluk waddled like a porcupine when it was out of the water. Its big flat tail was akin to that of a beaver, but spiked about the rump with enormous quills. It had a long, slender, blunt-ended horn on the top of its round head. The strange horn was flanked by huge clamshell ears. The eyes were two protuberant half-globes, black and moist and never blinking.

The Huluk's horn was covered with red and white spots. The fur of the Huluk was slick and mottled.

Three children were out digging roots one day, a little girl, a little boy, and an older boy. The girl wore a sleeveless dress of seal fur interlaced with braids of mountain-goat wool. Upon her head she wore a bobcat-fur cap. The two boys wore striped coats of tanned deerskin decorated with red beads. When the creature came out of the water, the little boy saw it first. He thought it was a beaver the size of a grizzly bear. He was a fearless boy, and the very idea of such a big beaver made him laugh.

"What are you laughing at?" asked his sister. "What do you see?"

The little boy pointed and exclaimed, "I like that creature's horn! I want it to belong to me!"

When his little sister saw it, she joined in the laughter. The horn was indeed very appealing. Together they ran toward the creature.

"Come back!" cried their older brother, understanding better the dangers of inexplicable beasts. He tried to run after his siblings, but his feet would not move, as though they were stuck in mud, or roots had grabbed him. The little ones did not listen to him.

The Huluk scooped up the little boy on its horn. Then it scooped up the little girl. They were taken into the water. From where the older child was standing, knee-deep in muck, it looked as though his siblings might have been impaled, but he wasn't sure, for they were obviously alive; he could still hear them laughing. As the creature slid into the lake and under the water's surface, carrying the two children on its horn, the older boy's legs were mysteriously freed from the muck, and he turned to flee.

He made it home and told his mother and father, "Brother and Sister have been carried away! The Tualatin lake-monster either drowned them or impaled them, I don't know which!"

Then the boy grew ill. He lay down on a mat in the longhouse. He sweated and moaned. His mother laid over him a cougarskin blanket and, as she did so, she saw that he was covered with red and purple spots.

~~~~~

The children's father was called Wawinxpa. Wawinxpa took a carved box from under a bench in the longhouse and opened it. He drew forth all his best clothes. He dressed himself in a shirt of tanned elkskin that his wife had decorated with beads and quills, tanned leggings and breechcloth, and new moccasins of deerhide with the fur intact.

His marmot-fur knife-belt was decorated with feathers from a white swan's back. His necklace consisted of bear claws, symbolic of warrior strength, plus the rare small shells of a shaman. He blacked his cheeks with pitch soot. Last of all, he put on a headdress. It was made of white swan feathers interspersed with red-and-black woodpecker feathers. The circlet of feathers stuck straight up from his head.

Wawinxpa went to the place where his youngest children had been taken away below the water. At the lake's edge he saw a big hole and followed the Huluk's tracks into a cave. When he came out the other side of the tunnel, he found himself in an enormous dry hollow beneath the lake. As he gazed about, he realized he had entered another world. The sky was made of shimmering earth, and trees were growing downward from the roof of the sky.

Off in the misty distance, he caught a glimpse of his children. They were clinging to the speckled horn of the monster, which trod slowly but steadily away. It moved awkwardly across pitted earth, dragging its tail and gouging the ground with its arrow-length quills, leaving a wide track that was easy to follow.

The father pursued the Huluk and his children through the dismal world up and down deep gullies. Time and again he caught sight of his children, but the monster was never closer or farther. It was always the same distance away. On the upper bank of the first gulley, Wawinxpa motioned with his hands and cried out for his children to let go of the horn and come to him.

His children clung fast and called back, "Father, we are different, different, different!"

The next day, from the top of the second gulley, he called to them again. But they only replied, "We are different, different!" as they held fast to the Huluk's horn. The monster waddled on and on, and though it never exerted itself, it managed somehow always to keep the same distance. The father grew increasingly despondent.

He made a camp each night in sheltered places low in one or another gulley. Five days he stayed in the strange land. Five times he ascended to a different gulley's ridge and called out, "Come to me, my children, come!" He could never catch up to them, and their reply was always the same.

After the fifth try, the father saw his children no more. He looked everywhere, but the Huluk was nowhere to be seen. Its wide trail vanished on a lava bed. Wawinxpa came out of the cave, into the good world, but the world seemed less good without his children. He went home and told his wife, "The Tualatin monster has taken our children to live under the mountain. All the trees in that place grow straight down out of the sky. I saw our children on the horn of the monster, but could not catch them."

Then he sat down with his wife and together they cried.

The older son lay sick with fever, sleeping fitfully. His mother prepared strong medicinal teas of herbs, crab-apple bark, and spruce sap, but nothing helped.

Through the night, Wawinxpa lay near his son. For a long time he could not sleep, for worrying that his last child would die.

Finally, Wawinxpa slept, and his night was filled with dreams. He drew dream-power into himself as he was sleeping. The next day his wife could not wake him. She watched her husband fretfully as she attended her sick son. Toward noon, Wawinxpa opened his eyes and said, "I have seen them in my dream. I will try again to bring them home."

Once more he made himself ready, wearing his many fine garments. He covered his forehead with black pitch. He made speckles on the rest of his face with red paint, white clay, and coal. Then, in the forest, he twisted a long hazel rope and tied one end around his waist. The other end he tied to a tree beside Lake Tualatin. He swam out to the middle of the lake and peered down.

Deep in the clear, clear water he saw his children on the horn of the monster. He called down into the waters, "Let go of the horn, my children, and swim up here to me!"

But they replied, "Father, we are different, different, different!"

He swam about the middle of the lake until he was weary, with just the feathers of his headdress sticking up. The whole time he prayed and prayed for assistance from good spirits. He prayed to the clouds, to the lake, to the mountains, to the trees, to the birds, and to the kindly spirit he had met in the forest when he came of age and which was always with him. By then he was so tired that he couldn't even swim to shore. He sank from view. He would have drowned, except that his wife came, dressed in a cedar-bark dress and a robe of interwoven seal, coon, and bobcat furs. She pulled on the hazel rope, drawing her husband out of the water. She raised him in her arms, wrapped him in a cougar-hide blanket, and held him fast until he was warm.

The next morning, Wawinxpa swam far out into the lake again, with just his headdress of swan and woodpecker feathers visible from the shore. He called to his children, but their answer was the same as before. On the fifth day, he saw that his children had changed markedly. Their hair was gone. Their eyes were half-globes of darkness without lids. Their bodies had merged into one speckled body with two heads.

The Changelings

He called down to them, "Children, swim up here to me!"

Both heads spoke at once, saying, "Father, I am different, different, different!"

~~~~~

Wawinxpa's five days of prayers, and his rigorous ascetic performance in the lake, assisted in the recovery of his one remaining child. The boy had only white scars to show that the Huluk had seen him. On that last day of the father's prayer, fast, and swimming, the son came with his mother to the lakeshore. Together they pulled on the hazel cord.

For the last time Wawinxpa was drawn out of the water. He clung to his wife and son, and his feather headdress fell to the ground. All he could say was, "The children belong forever to the Huluk. Weep, my wife; weep, my only son; weep, for they are different, different, different."

When the Woman Chief Was Young

A Legend of Crater Lake

〰

THE CHIEF OF the Klamath nation was wise and valiant. As he grew older, he became a man of considerable wealth. One day he looked about and saw that he had achieved all his life's goals but one. He had no son to be his heir. With heavy heart he asked, "To whom will I teach the ways of justice?" In his distress, he sought the counsel of three prophets who knew the ways of divine beings as intimately as the chief knew the ways of mortals. These wise men put their heads together and spoke with the great spirits of sun, earth, wind, and water. They perceived that come autumn, at the time of the wapato harvest, the chief's wife would bear a child worthy to be his heir.

The following autumn, a child was born. To the chief's chagrin, the child was a baby girl.

As she grew, the chief, remembering the prophesy of the wise men, saw to the instruction of his daughter. She learned to hunt; she rode in battle; she learned the ways of wisdom in mediating disputes and rendering fair judgments. Her name was Chao the Antelope, though many years later she was called Wolkotska the Cougar.

She was as lovely as the dawn, and the Klamaths loved her for her courage and kindness. That she went clad in the garments of a hunter only heightened the effect of her beauty. One day she was hunting in the mountains and was seen by Llao, ruler of the demons of Crater Lake and of the world below. From his lofty throne at the lake's western edge, he observed the boyish maiden for a long while, admiring her tracking skills. Everything about her appealed to him: her quill-worked shirt of antelope skin, her mantle of cougar fur, her high beaded moccasins, the colorfully fletched arrows in her quiver. The demon-king came down from his rocky throne and said to Chao, "Live with me at the center of the world. You will be wealthy beyond dreams as queen of powerful armies." Chao looked up from her tracking and laughed. She refused him. He dared not take her by force, as she gleamed with a personal magic, and she was armed with a bow, sharp arrows, and a knife.

The following day, the demon-king was seen coming across a meadow toward the Klamath village. The people saw his big grey face, his horned ears, his tough sinewy arms and taloned claws, and they were greatly alarmed. When he smiled, his teeth were not reassuring, and when he hailed the chief with friendly words, the harshness of his voice was disheartening.

Llao entered into a bargaining with Chao's father and mother. Because he was a god, he was able to offer good hunting and fishing, fair weather, and large harvests in exchange for Chao. In addition, he would provide personal wealth: dentalia shells for use as money, obsidian for making spear tips and arrowheads, copper beads from under the earth, and a great many furs of black otters and white foxes.

The chief said, "As you can see, my daughter is not like other maidens; she is also my son and will rule the Klamaths when I have gone to the land of the spirits. I do not wish to anger you, yet must ask that you turn your heart to another."

Llao glowered silently for some while before he replied, "You will regret this." He strode away across the meadow.

~~~~~

The following autumn there was a poor wapato harvest, and other roots were just as hard to find. Then came a terrifyingly cold winter. The game fled to warmer climes and the salmon could not be expected until late in spring, by which time many Klamaths would starve to death. The chief called together the three prophets. They said, "What mortal can oppose the dark god Llao, ruler of the underworld? We must seek a champion, and who better than Skell, king of the skyworld?"

Skell's lodge was beyond the Yamsay River. As it happened, he had one day seen Chao running in pursuit of a deer. She hunted far and wide to assist her hungry people, so had wandered into Skell's country seeking meat. He fell in love with the huntress at once and secretly followed her to her village.

The deer that Chao carried to her people was insufficient to feed everyone. Skell saw his chance to win his way into her heart. He commanded his eagles to fetch a large number of hares and bring them to the hungry village at once. When golden eagles appeared from every part of the forest with their offerings, the Klamaths were astonished and delighted. Then Skell came forth and said to the chief, "My heart aches for your daughter. You did wisely to refuse her hand to Llao, for as his queen she would have lived miserably in the darkness of the world-cavern, worshipped by slavering monsters. At my side, she will become queen of sun and sky. Flowers will arise in her footsteps. She will rule the children of the fox, the deer, and all that dwells in the forest; it shall be as though she were their only mother, before whom all life bows."

When the Woman Chief Was Young

The chief felt despair welling inside him. He had hoped to seek out Skell as a champion for his people against the malignant Llao, but now he had to risk angering even the good god, saying, "Great Skell, once I was without an heir, and I made sacrifices and supplications to the spirits of sky and earth, wind and water, and you were yourself among the divinities whose intercession I requested. Through my wise men I was promised an heir, and Chao was sent to me. I asked, 'Is it possible the gods have made an error?' and I answered, 'Indeed not; this girl will be my heir.' This being so, how can I send her to live in the sky? I am old and will soon rest forever. Chao must remain with her people, who have already accepted her as my son. As chief of the Klamaths, she will choose her spouse, and not be chosen."

Skell said, "Well do I remember your prayers and sacrifices, but even gods may err, for each of us has his own design. Little did I know what giving you Chao would mean for me, or for my rival Llao. Know this, chief of the Klamaths: that for the sake of your daughter, the huntress Chao, there will be war between the upper world and the lower world. When gods do battle, mortals invariably feel the tragic repercussions of divine severity."

Thereafter Skell took it upon himself to protect the Klamaths from Llao's hostilities. When Llao called forth clouds of icy storms, Skell called forth warm sunlight to soften the stormy blows. When Llao's forces frightened away all the game of the region, Skell sent troops of his own game to sacrifice themselves before the arrows of Klamath hunters. When Llao's underworld fiends cast a blight upon essential roots and berries, Skell surreptitiously arranged sunlit meadows with plenitude, and revealed these sites to Chao.

The Klamaths moved their village to Klamath Lake, and discovered Skell's meadows nearby. Here Llao's evil influences were weakest, due to Skell's handiwork. The fish in this lake were beyond Llao's command. He became increasingly annoyed with Skell for negating his efforts to starve and punish the Klamaths.

One night, when Llao's frustrations were piqued, the demon-king called forth a large number of his shadowy, monstrous soldiers. They gathered with the demon-king upon his rock, and Llao said to them, "For as long as Skell lives as the protector of the Klamaths, I will not be able to slay the old chief and steal away Chao for my underworld bride. Come! Let us thwart Skell!"

For five days Llao and his soldiers chanted war songs and beat huge bass drums made from the skins of tattooed men. Demons arrived in increasing numbers from the bottom of the round lake and from the black depths of caves, bearing clubs and knives and savage faces, waving their knotted fists, eager for a fight. All this while, Llao breathed forth a fetid smokiness that spread across the land.

At the end of the five days, the world was as dark by day as by night, as choking as a cedar lodge with its smoke-holes closed tight. Then Llao sent his legions into Skell's country to wreak havoc.

As Skell was a divinity of sunlight, the smoky darkness bewildered him. He called upon his legions of foxes, eagles, mountain goats, elk, bear, antelope, and cougars, but all these were made sleepy and befuddled by the incessant night. They feared the smoke as a harbinger of fire, and knew not which way to run. Meanwhile, the shades that Llao brought from the underworld roved about the land unchecked. When they came to the lodge of Skell, they dragged him out into the blinding smoke. They were delighted to discover that the hellish black fog had rendered Skell as helpless and bewildered as his animals. They bludgeoned him with their clubs, laughing hideously as they rent him piece from piece with their dreadful knives. Maliciously they carved out Skell's immortal heart and ran howling and hooting back to Llao's land, bearing the beating heart with them.

The conjured smoke dispersed from the countryside. A natural night descended, filled with stars and a fat bright moon reflecting on the cold waters of Llao's perfectly round lake. Llao and his legions gathered on the throne-rock, screeching their victory chants. Then Llao threw the beating heart of Skell into the lake, where gigantic, brilliantly red crawfishes caught it and threw it one to another. They played with the heart of Skell as though it were a ball at a festival. Llao and his army sat along the cliffs cheering and encouraging the moon-lit sport of the clawed monsters.

The game went on all night long. At dawn, the huntress Chao appeared at the eastern edge of the lake, opposite the side of Llao's Rock. She called across the waters in a chiding manner, "How weak you are! Can't you throw Skell's heart any higher than that? The smallest child in my village could throw it higher!"

The crawfish were insulted. Llao's legion chanted to the players, "Throw it higher! Throw it higher!" Skell's heart was given a mighty toss from a crawfish's claw. When another crawfish caught it, Chao laughed mockingly, and said, "Is that so high? Oh, such weaklings!" Each time Chao chided them, the crawfish threw the heart still higher. Then an eagle streaked across the sky, caught Skell's heart in its talons, and sped over the lake's surface pursued by crawfishes. It dropped the beating heart into Chao's upstretched hands.

The huntress immediately fled with the prize. Llao shouted, "After her! After her!" and all the legions chased her through the wilderness toward the land of the River Yamsay.

The huntress was as swift as the antelope for which she was named. The rising sun burned the eyes of her pursuers. Wolves and bears leapt at the demons with claws and teeth, while foxes and deer led them astray. With this assistance, Chao left her pursuers far behind and came alone to the lodge of Skell. Outside the lodge, Skell's pale, lifeless limbs lay strewn about. His head was upside-down beside a stump. His torso lay before the door of the lodge. Chao carefully put his body back together, affixing limbs to torso and placing his head just so. She then inserted the heart in his chest, so that the god sprang back to life.

~~~~~

For the span of half a moon, Chao nursed the sky-god, during which time Llao's minions continued to terrorize the band of Klamaths. The tribe moved from Klamath Lake to Little Klamath Lake in their effort to avoid the demon-king. Throughout this time the Klamaths had no news of their princess and grieved that both she and Skell had been slain in the war against Llao.

One night the demons of Llao surrounded the harried village at Little Klamath Lake and took the people prisoner. They bound every-one with hazel rope and marched them away. The old chief and his wife they whipped with a cord. All through the night they tramped toward Crater Lake; men and women, old and young—all were so dispirited and weakened by weeks of poor nourishment that they could do nothing in their own behalf.

When they reached the lake, the people saw against the moonlight the terrible shadow of Llao atop his great rock. In a bellowing, thun-derous voice he demanded, "Where have you hidden Chao the Beautiful One, my chosen bride? Reveal her at once, or you shall all be fed to my crawfishes!"

Hearing their name called, the crawfish-monsters raised their beady-eyed faces above the water and created a froth in the starlit waters about them, stirring with their clacking claws. Yet the terror of this vision was not as effective as it might otherwise have been, for the Klamaths realized for the first time, by Llao's own demand, that he had failed to capture or slay their princess! The old chief stepped forth, his back bleeding from the whipping the devils had given him. He said, "We have not seen Chao for half a moon. Perhaps she is licking her wounds in some secret place, we don't know. When she is able, she will return and wage an avenging battle against you, like a good son."

The Klamaths laughed and hollered in agreement and began to sing the name of Chao. The devils backed away, as they disliked the sound of human laughter. It was then that the spirit-canoe appeared in the east of the lake, and in it stood the huntress Chao and the sky-god Skell. Skell flew out of the canoe and over the lake, landing alongside Llao on the throne-rock. They were shadows against the moon, locked arm in arm in deadly combat. They fell to their sides still embracing, and no one could tell whose knife it was that glinted on the left and whose knife glinted on the right.

Chao stepped out of the spirit-canoe and confronted five devils. She unleashed two arrows before the devils fled. She hurried to her mother and father and untied their hands, and soon everyone was untying someone else. Just as their spirits were highest, the Klamaths were stunned to hear the thunderous voice of Llao cry out, "Feast, my crawfishes, upon the arms of Skell!"

The shadowy king threw two severed body parts into the lake, which the crawfish rent into small pieces as the waters grew black with the god's blood.

The dark figure atop the rock bent down to again hack at the corpse. Then he stood and cried out, "Feast, my crawfishes, upon the legs of Skell!"

The monsters caught the falling limbs and began to devour them with rapacious delight.

A third time the Klamaths heard the horrible bellowing: "Feast, my beauties, upon the heart and torso of Skell!" as he threw the greater part of his foe into the roiling waters.

The hearts of the Klamath people were dashed low. The devils, no longer cowed, came forth from the places where Chao had sent them hiding. However, in the next moment, the Klamaths were cheering excitedly, for they saw that it was Skell upon the rock! Skell laughed in his own handsome voice, crying out, "Last of all I give to you the head of your master Llao!"

As Llao's head struck the surface of the water, it was miraculously transformed into Wizard Island. His gaping mouth became the island's burning crater. The crawfishes, in horror of having eaten their king, sank away into the unnatural depths of the lake, never to be seen again.

The devilish warriors along the lakeshore ran forth planning to avenge their ruler by battling the Klamaths, who were all unarmed save Chao. But as they ran forward, they began to dissipate in the rising dawn. Their shadowy forms faded into morning's mist, which clung a while to the surface of the lake, and then was gone.

~~~~~

It was not long after these events that the father of Chao died peacefully in the fulfillment of his life. His wife's spirit followed after him in due course. For many years thereafter, in the long-past age that is today but an echo of a dream, the Maklak clan of Klamaths dwelt among their lakes and vales, ruled by a noble and wise woman chief whose footfalls in the forest were as light as Wolkotska the Cougar, who was as gracefully fleetfooted as Chao the Antelope, and who was beloved of all her people.

Red Wolf's Daughter and Bloody Chief's Son
The Romance of Wallowa Lake

※

A FIERCE BATTLE was engaged in the snowy forest of pine and tamaracks above Wallowa Lake. Red Wolf's Chute-pa-lu band whirled ravenously in the midst of the ambushed Blackfoot scouting party.

For long moons, Blackfeet had been striving to displace Red Wolf's Chute-pa-lu Nez Perce from their ancient fishing and hunting grounds. With a thousand streams, and rivers, and lakes, it was good country, worth a fight. When the interlopers first began troubling the established tribe, it seemed they could not hope to succeed and would soon return to their lands defeated.

All the early battles fell to the valor of Red Wolf and his courageous followers, familiar as they were with the region. But by degrees, as the Blackfeet had increasingly mastered the forest, it became more and more difficult for the Nez Perces to surprise the foe. A great leader had arisen among the Blackfeet. That man was Bloody Chief, a clever tactician who drew more Blackfeet from beyond Shining Mountain to join him. Increasingly, it was Red Wolf's men who were surprised by ambushes.

On this day, however, the Nez Perces met with good luck. A band of eight enemy scouts came running up the forest slope away from the lake, shouting among themselves about something hideous they had seen. They made so much ridiculous noise that they gave themselves away while still at some distance. Then they stopped short, shocked to discover they had fled straight into the arms of Red Wolf and his warriors.

The cluster of Blackfoot scouts spun about as though they intended to run back the way they had come. Yet they were seemingly even more afraid of retreating in that direction than they were of facing impossible odds against the Nez Perces. In that moment of indecision, the Nez Perces were upon them. Red Wolf swung his long warclub of polished hardwood beveled along one edge and inlaid with the teeth of wolves. His opponent tried ineffectually to deflect a blow. In the next moment, blood and brain spattered freshly tramped snow. The Blackfoot fell backward and lay with tongue and one eye hanging out.

After a few hard breaths, it was done. All the birds had flown away. The forest was silent save for the harsh breathing of the victors. The Blackfeet all lay dead or dying, whereas Red Wolf had but one man down. Red Wolf stalked amidst the Blackfoot corpses, saw one man not yet fully dead, and bashed his skull. Then he knelt beside an injured Nez Perce. He looked at the man's gaping wound, took the warrior's arm, and said, "Press your hand here, so." Then he motioned four men to carry the one, and they started down the hill. When they reached the snowline, they knew their village was near.

One of Red Wolf's warriors said, "I wonder what those scouts were running from?"

"Strong spirits guard this place," said Red Wolf. "They are Chute-pa-lu spirits, angered by the presence of Blackfeet."

His men did not contradict this, for they hoped Red Wolf's opinion was inspired by the spirit-power that was in him. They would not like to see him proven wrong.

At a bonfire in the center of the village, the people gathered for a communal feast. They ate trout, crawfish, and fernbrake. It was a good meal, but nothing compared to what in better times was expected from the rich forest. With the present war, there had been little opportunity to hunt elk or bear.

As the warriors told expansive versions of that day's successful battle, the tribe became cheerful. Each man in turn was encouraged to tell of the battle from his point of view. With every retelling, the story was embellished and improved. The part about the Blackfeet petrified in their tracks, too frightened to either attack or run away, won screeches of laughter.

But underlying the momentary cheerfulness of women, old men, and children was a continuous thrum of fear. Reflected on the waters of icy Wallowa Lake was the greater bonfire of Blackfeet on the farther shore. They were dancing and hollering and pounding drums. Perhaps as yet they did not know that eight of their men had been killed. When they learned of it, they would seek swift vengeance. The sound of the Blackfoot celebration reached the Chute-pa-lu, muted but clear, and Chute-pa-lu laughter was insufficient to shut out the noise of the big gathering of their foe.

The sorry fact was, the Nez Perce village had lost the majority of its young warriors, whereas the Blackfeet seemed to spring in ever increasing numbers.

Red Wolf declined to tell his version of the victory. He was not able to eat. He accepted a carved juniper trough with a fat portion of trout, but could only look at it as though it were something he disliked. He stood from the circle of his men and walked away without a word, carrying the trough with him. All knew by his moodiness and demeanor that they must not call after him. He faded into the darkness outside the circle of firelight.

~~~~~

In a tipi near an old spruce, the injured man lay upon a bearskin robe, his lower body covered with a blanket of marmot skins. He was not young, though he was famous for the many adventures of his youth. He was proud to be called Old Strength. Often Red Wolf had tried to convince him to remain in the village as its guard. Always he replied, "What! Like an old man? Let's go kill Blackfeet!" Now, if he recovered, the muscle of his arm was so deeply cut that he would never again be strong enough to fight.

Old Strength's bare chest glistened with sweat, though the early autumn evening was chill. A small fire burned in the center of the floor. A trail of smoke rose in a thin line and escaped where the tipi's braces joined. Old Strength was attended by Red Wolf's daughter, Wahluna, a shamanic healer. She was singing a magic song that went, "Healing spirits, healing spirits, see this man, see him." It was like a lullaby.

From a medicine bag she drew forth herbs, which she pounded in a mortar, adding pure lakewater until she had a green paste. This she smeared on Old Strength's broad, ragged wounds. There were two wounds, made with a single thrust of a spear that had bared a rib at his side and parted the flesh of the inner muscle of his right arm. Wahluna pressed boiled moss into the paste upon the wounds. Over the curative concoction she bound muskrat hides. Through all her endeavors, Old Strength scarcely winced, though his jaw quivered with pain.

When Red Wolf entered the tipi, Wahluna ceased her soft chant. The wounded man tried to rise, as it was improper to lie down in the presence of Red Wolf. Wahluna put her hand on his chest to hold him down. She said, "If you move, you will not live long." Red Wolf sat on the ground near the sad-looking warrior. He broke a piece of the tender trout and held it to Old Strength's mouth. At first Old Strength turned his head away, but he turned back with moist eyes and let himself be fed. Wahluna took up her healing lullaby while Old Strength was fed like a baby.

"You are Red Wolf, and should not serve me so," said Old Strength.

Red Wolf said, "You served my father, and you have served me. You were like an uncle when I was small. Haven't the Blackfeet killed all your sons? Didn't your wife die of grief? Who are your relatives now? A chief must be every man's father. Wahluna must be every man's mother."

At this, Old Strength smiled in earnest. Not only was he deeply touched, but he was amused to think of the young princess as an aging warrior's mother. She helped prop him against a rolled fur so he could sit up. She pulled the marmot blanket to his shoulders. Old Strength grew extremely serious. He asked, "How long, Red Wolf, can we go on? We are slowly being picked off, while more Blackfeet come from their nation into ours. Today we were fortunate. But what will happen tomorrow?"

"Tomorrow?" Red Wolf echoed, and his gaze rose along the little column of smoke until he spotted one star through the opening where the poles joined. "Today, the warriors are filled with boasts and hold their hands above their heads. Tomorrow, it may be that their shoulders will sag with the weight of sorrows. You were my father's counselor. Should I pretend in your presence that things are well? Tomorrow? There is only today, Old Strength. And today we are victorious."

Having said so much, Red Wolf left the tipi of Old Strength. He stood alone by Wallowa Lake, listening dejectedly to chants and drums of Blackfeet on the far shore.

~~~~~~

Wahluna covered Old Strength with the blanket, then looked about until she found a well-worn buffalo robe and laid that on him too. She asked the warrior, "Old Strength, why do the Blackfeet fight us? Why do we fight the Blackfeet?"

Old Strength replied, "You are too young to understand."

"I am old enough to be your mother," she teased.

"Ha! Well then, little mother, you are not a child after all. So I will tell you that not one of us can know the reason why men kill men. Your grandfather, who died when you were little, of the same sickness that carried away your mother, was called Red Wolf like your father. He was a great buffalo hunter. Today we lake people do not go to the place of the buffalo, but when I was young, we went every summer. There were many Blackfeet that came from their place beyond the buffalo grounds. We watched each other killing buffalo, and when they made a mistake, we laughed. When we failed, they made light of us and hooted. Then they stole some of our horses, thinking themselves clever. We stole them back, and some of theirs as well.

"Somehow it came about that every year when we went to hunt buffalo, we went to kill Blackfeet as well. They had the best horses, so we had to be smarter. We found out what route they took to reach the buffalo grounds. One year we went early. From a high point, overlooking a narrow canyon, we were able to kill very many Blackfeet. Among the Chute-pa-lu, however, not one man fell! It is my thought, little mother, that if some of us had died on that day, the Blackfeet would not hate us so much. They have avenged themselves many times since, but they remember that first humiliation, when your grandfather led us home to the mountain country, bringing Blackfoot horses! We built great fires and danced for days and nights. Oh! Those were good days, little mother. I miss those days so much."

Wahluna let Old Strength sleep. She went out to see if she could find her father. But Red Wolf had vanished into the forest to commune with his own heart. Under the starry sky, Wahluna felt alone on the earth. She could hear her people laughing and telling stories. So too she could hear the whooping Blackfeet across the lake. They did not seem entirely real to her. They were ghosts from a bad, bad dream.

She went among the thickly draping willows at the lake's edge. From the willow roots a stream leapt forth into the lake, its rippling music erasing all the other sounds of night. Hidden as she was amidst draping leaves, Wahluna's sad loneliness became a boon of solitude while she watched the moon reflected on the water.

Against the moon she saw a nighthawk dipping and flitting. She thought to herself, "My soul is with the nighthawk. I am up there dipping and flitting. What does my soul seek? It seeks happiness and peace. Can you hear me, spirit of Wallowa? Does not the bloodshed hurt you, as it hurts me? I call to you, spirit of the lake! I call to the Mother-spirit and the Father-spirit. I call to the tree-spirits and the wind-spirits. I pray to all of you, give me strength, give me wisdom. Show me by what means I may stop the killing. No price is too great for me to pay! I would be a slave to the Blackfeet if that would bring peace. I will give my life!"

As she spoke, she saw the waters stirring in the light of moon and stars. Then she spotted an empty skin-canoe at the lake's edge. As she had not seen it a moment before, it seemed to her a thing materialized from a vision. She took the appearance of the canoe to be an invitation to go upon the lake.

Red Wolf's Daughter and Bloody Chief's Son

Wahluna paddled silently through the darkness. She crossed the lake to the enemy village. She left with such stillness the Nez Perces did not hear her go, nor did the Blackfeet detect her arrival until she was within the circle of a bonfire. At the sight of this beautiful maiden appearing as though from nowhere, celebrant drummers ceased beating their tomtoms. Singers stilled their voices. The only sound was the crackling of the fire as Wahluna approached Bloody Chief, who sat crosslegged on a blanket alongside Tlesca, his son. Each wore a beautifully woven robe of feathers, quills, and fibers, the insignias of their rank.

"I am Wahluna, princess of my tribe, come to speak to a great chief," she began. "Many of the young men of my tribe have been slain. I despair for the survival of my people. Today the remnant of our fighters met Blackfoot scouts lurking in our forest. All those scouts were slain. It has made my people joyous, but such joy cannot be sustained, for our women have long sung songs of mourning.

"I hear your followers gasp with anger to learn of our luck in today's battle, though I speak of these things not to boast. Tomorrow, you may seek revenge for eight lives. Perhaps my family and my people, with all that I have known in this life, will be exterminated once and for all. Yet I have come to you to say, 'Have pity!' for there can be no greatness in slaying old men, women, and small children, which is nearly all that is left of us now. If you will allow me to take to my father your offer of peace, it may be that we can learn to share the bounty of the forest and the lake without so great an enmity."

Bloody Chief barely considered her words before he answered, "What cowardly people send a girl to beg? Such a tribe merits death!"

But Tlesca was impressed with the maiden. Though a great warrior by necessity, his spirit was inclined to gentleness. He said, "Father, open your heart to her words. This maiden bravely loves her people. As for me, I am moved beyond my capacity for speech. Never again will I kill one of her people."

Having made such a bold statement, he stood from the blanket on which he had been sitting. He removed his cloak of authority as he stepped to Wahluna's side.

Bloody Chief made a growling sound in his throat, for he had often wished for a harsher son. Even so, he greatly loved Tlesca, and could not dismiss his son's words. He said, "My son, one day you must become a great chief. You cannot rely on kindheartedness to rule. Her people are mere dogs. Come! Put on your robe, for this girl must die."

Tlesca was insistent. "We have battled Red Wolf's bravest warriors. Remember how Red Wolf fought, days on end, to save his people? I recall how impressed you were! For many weeks we gave him no opportunity to capture game; we harried him until he was weak from hunger. We even saw him stagger! Even then, when he was at his weakest, who was brave enough to fight him face to face? I alone answered his challenge. He fought like a cougar. With his warclub, he broke my shoulder, which was long in healing.

"How often I think of that day! Many of our warriors fell before Red Wolf as they rushed forth to draw me away when you, my father, commanded me not to fight one-handed. Do you say we were routed by a dog, my father? Did my shoulder hurt because I was weaker than a dog?

"No, my father, Red Wolf is a noble warrior, and this maiden who has come before us is noble too. Look! I have taken off my robe of authority to place it about her shoulders! See? It suits her well. She looks as powerful as a warrior!"

Bloody Chief closed his eyes and thought. The people gathered nearby were motionless. Then Bloody Chief raised his eyes and addressed the crowd. "My son speaks well. I have heard his words. Therefore will I rise and place my robe upon his."

Wahluna stood straight and tall as Bloody Chief wrapped his robe about her. The two robes were tokens of a promise of peace, to be worn before her father Red Wolf so that he would know for whom she spoke of truce.

As she turned to leave the circle of firelight, no one followed. Prince Tlesca strode away into the woods above the lake. Yet when Wahluna arrived at her canoe by the lakeside, there stood Tlesca, who had hurried to skirt the edge of the village, to reach the lake in secret. He wished to see Wahluna off without detection. He said, "Wahluna, truly my heart is made lighter in your presence."

She replied, "I, too, was moved by your manly beauty and the fairness of your speech. But you must not hope the two of us will become as one. If my father suspected my love for a Blackfoot prince, he would rise up and fight to the death. If your father thought you loved a Chute-pa-lu princess, he would exterminate my people rather than give his blessing to such a union. You must turn your heart toward a Blackfoot maiden. As for me, I have sworn my life to the spirit of Wallowa Lake in exchange for a prosperous peace for our peoples."

"Blackfoot girls are beautiful and many have expressed their love for Tlesca," he admitted. "Even so, my heart seeks none but Wahluna."

She said, "What you desire cannot be."

"It may be that we must keep our feelings to ourselves," he said, taking her by the arm for fear that she would leave too soon. "But Wahluna, listen. We can meet secretly in our canoes on dark nights in the middle of the lake. No one will suspect. When I wish to see you,

you will hear me make the sound of a coyote. When you wish to see me, call to me in the voice of the owl. By these signals we will come together and speak."

"I cannot promise such a thing," she said, though already she knew she would lay awake nights listening for the coyote call. Then, warm in the cloaks of chief and prince, she knelt into her canoe and paddled to her village.

~~~~~

The successful peace talks that ensued were greatly facilitated by Wahluna's previously unsuspected skill as a mediator. Many meetings were required. Many bad feelings were mollified. For six moons, as the truce held, Red Wolf and Bloody Chief met in neutral places in the mountains, bringing with them none but Wahluna and Tlesca, whose natures were more giving than those of their hardened fathers.

Many times Wahluna despaired, fearing these two men would never acknowledge that each saw greatness in the other. Many nights she lay awake thinking she was failing at mediation, and the soothing speeches of Tlesca were failing also. So too it was painful to see the youth she secretly loved, under conditions that demanded that neither give evidence of the affection that intensified daily.

One evening as she lay worrying in her tipi, she heard a coyote singing. At first she did not heed the call, for it sounded like a true coyote. When it called again, she thought it sounded as though it were in the middle of the lake. Only then did she rise swiftly to slip to the lakeside, where she called out like an owl. She knelt in her canoe, which lay hidden in shallows amidst overhanging willows.

She paddled toward the center of the lake and stopped alongside Tlesca. They reached their hands toward one another to pull their canoes closer, and Tlesca said, "I am in an agony of lonely sorrow. I see you only in the presence of our fathers. When can we tell our peoples of our love?"

Wahluna, too, was steeped in melancholy. She said, "I have sworn myself to the spirit of the lake. I offered everything to this spirit, even my life, in exchange for peace between our tribes. For six moons there has been no arrow exchanged by Blackfeet and Nez Perces. By this I know the spirit has heeded my prayer. Were I to accept all that is in your heart, the lake would only take it from me, for all that I receive belongs to the spirit of the Wallowa."

"If it is so," said Tlesca, "then what good is my life? My heart is yours even now. I will fight this spirit!"

"You must not say so!" exclaimed Wahluna.

The water had become agitated. As they gazed at the dark surface, a slowly funneling maelstrom encircled them and caused their canoes to turn around and around. Tlesca gaped in amazement. Wahluna said, not to Tlesca but to the spirit of the lake, "Do not grow angry, O Spirit of Wallowa!"

At her plea, the water grew still, and Tlesca said softly, "If the power of this lake possesses all that is yours, then this power possesses me. I will not fight it, but will share in your destiny."

When the most difficult matters of the truce were settled, joy at last arose among the Nez Perces. One morning a great many children, women, and men, old and young, arrived from the Blackfoot village singing songs of friendship. The men brought fresh-killed deer and bear hunted in the mountains. The women bore fish trapped in streams.

Throughout the festivities, Wahluna and Tlesca exchanged meaningful glances whenever they thought no one could see them flirting.

Wahluna and other Nez Perce women assisted the Blackfoot wives and daughters in preparing a great feast. It seemed to Wahluna that a real affection had developed between the tribes. She began to allow herself to hope her fondness for the Blackfoot prince might after all be revealed without reawakening anger.

As the afternoon progressed into evening, Wahluna became bolder when casting glances at Tlesca, and several Nez Perce girls noticed. They began to whisper, "There is something going on between Wahluna and that beautiful young Blackfoot."

The gossip spread throughout the village. Soon all the Nez Perce women were considering the possibilities. Some were joyful at the thought; a few were jealous, for they had been trying to catch a glance from the prince without success. Not everyone agreed such a match would be a good idea, for the friendship between the two peoples was as yet very new and untested. There remained many suspicions and ill-healed wounds of grief because of sons lost in battle.

Divided opinions fueled the rumors, which soon spread to the Blackfoot women as well.

In evening's dusk, when half the people were done feasting, several women began to gamble with engraved beaver teeth, tossing them like dice. A Blackfoot woman, tall and handsome, won a Nez Perce woman's woven conical hat. Sorry to have wagered the hat, the stout Nez Perce woman said, "Take these moccasins instead, for I love that hat."

The tall woman answered, "Your moccasins are worn thin; I'll keep this."

They argued back and forth until the Nez Perce woman leapt at the Blackfoot and knocked her to the ground. They rolled in the dust while the other gambling women broke into opposing camps to cheer and encourage their champions. Blackfeet cheered the tall woman; Nez Perces cheered the woman who was stout.

Into this fracas Tlesca strode in order to separate the women. The hat was damaged during this wrestling match. The woman who had won the hat spat on the ground and said, "You think your princess is worthy of our prince? They will never marry!"

The Nez Perce woman shot back, "Who says she wants to marry him? As our young men have become bones for wolves to gnaw, so should this haughty chief's son be killed and left to rot in the forest!"

The women tried to get at each other again, but Tlesca held them apart, alarmed though he was by what they were saying.

Bloody Chief and Red Wolf had all this while been smoking the pipe together. The women's quarrel was on everyone's tongues except for these two chiefs, who knew not what to say.

After a long silence between them, Bloody Chief finally spoke. "My son's heart reaches for your daughter. He is a great warrior and will rule after me. Your Wahluna has proven herself a great mediator. Who else is their equal? Perhaps we should not stand in their way."

Red Wolf and his people had suffered so long at the hands of Blackfoot warriors, it was painful to accept such a marriage. Yet Red Wolf was a wise man and came to a sensible conclusion. He said, "Yes, I too have heard of their secret meetings. I confess I turned my face and hoped it was not so. Yet now, if in truth Wahluna's heart reaches out to Tlesca, she may go with him to his lodge."

In days that followed, Red Wolf sent runners to announce the wedding of Wahluna and Tlesca to friends among the Cayuse, Wenatchees, and Yakamas. A three-day wedding feast was planned. People came into the Nez Perce village from far and near, for the joining of two famous families that were former rivals was a great thing and deserved to be attended by many.

The Blackfoot village was empty of all but a few dogs and ponies, for all had left to participate in the extravagant affair with the Nez Perces. At sunset on the first day of the feast, the newly joined couple set out in a canoe to head for Tlesca's lodge across the lake, where they could be alone. People stood on the shore and the hillside watching the beautiful couple paddle across Wallowa Lake, with the high mountains forming a dark backdrop against a fading sky of red dusk.

Halfway across the lake, the lake's calm was disrupted. At first there were only mild ripples upon the water, which caused the boat to wobble. But the ripples rose into a roil, so that the canoe was greatly endangered. Tlesca dropped the paddle and clung to Wahluna. They spoke to one another earnestly and did not look frightened. The tumultuous waters rose in waves, spinning the little skin canoe around and around.

Old Strength, the aged warrior, shoved one of the largest canoes into the lake and jumped inside, intending to assist the couple who were caught in the inexplicable maelstrom. Red Wolf leapt into the big canoe in front of Old Strength. Other Nez Perce and Blackfeet, including Bloody Chief, followed close behind. All were eager to save Wahluna and Tlesca before their vessel was swamped and carried under.

As the would-be helpers neared, Wahluna cried out, "Old Strength! Father! Come no closer!"

Tlesca called, "Father, hold back!"

The tiny fleet of canoes halted. The little skin canoe continued to turn around and around as Wahluna called out in calm resignation, "This is what I promised the spirit of the lake in exchange for peace between our tribes!"

Red Wolf's Daughter and Bloody Chief's Son

Tlesca added, "With open eyes, I have sworn to share Wahluna's fate! Live in peace, my father and my father-in-law! Do not fight again! Do not grieve too long for us!"

The waters abruptly parted, revealing a monstrous creature. Its furred neck rose higher and higher. Its head was like the head of a gigantic pony, with the downturned horns of a buffalo. It swept its gaze from side to side, watching the fleet of canoes as hollering Nez Perces and Blackfeet paddled madly for their respective shores. Then the creature raised its long, heavy tail out of the water and thrashed it downward, hard upon the tiny canoe, cutting it in half.

Wahluna and Tlesca continued to cling tightly to one another as they were thrown into the water. Even now they conveyed no fear of dying; they offered no useless struggle. They closed their eyes, placed their faces each upon the shoulder of the other, and the quickening maelstrom sucked them down and down forever.

The dragon dove after them into the funnel of water.

All grew still beneath night's canopy of stars. Only a few small bubbles broke the surface of lake, to mark the passing of beast and lovers.

~~~~~~

At dawn, when it was certain the lovers were truly lost, there arose among Nez Perce women a continuous lamentation lasting many days. Their grief inspired many new songs of sorrow. Some sang that Wahluna had been taken from them because she had wrongly loved the enemy, while others sang in guilty sadness that all had been punished for feeling critical of the marriage, because their small hearts continued to despise Blackfeet.

Bloody Chief believed he had lost his son because his people tried to conquer the Nez Perces in order to take possession of their lake and forest, and the monster had come to punish the Blackfeet for their greed. Feeling nothing beyond self-blame and sorrow, Bloody Chief led his people away from the accursed lake that had stolen his son.

The Blackfeet left Wallowa afoot and on horseback. Their heads hung low; they moaned with grievous sorrow. Along the way, they stopped but once, at a crossroad where Red Wolf and Old Strength stood waiting to bid last farewells.

Although neither Bloody Chief nor Red Wolf could find words, they understood one another through shared loss. Red Wolf stepped forth to the side of Bloody Chief's pony and tried to return to him the pair of robes that had been given to Wahluna by Tlesca and Bloody Chief. But the Blackfoot chief would not take them. Red Wolf had thought this might occur. He handed the robes to Old Strength. Then he removed from the strap at his side the famous warclub inlaid with wolf teeth. This he gave to Bloody Chief as a parting gift. Only then did the long line of Blackfeet continue on their way to their country beyond the Shining Mountain, to return nevermore to the Land of Many Waters.

Lake of the Jealous Women

A Tale of Glacier National Park

⫯

ONE OF THE most beautiful of the innumerable lakes of Montana's Glacier National Park is known by the unpretty name McDermott Lake, with Mount Gould reflected in its glacial waters. The Blackfeet used to call this Beaver Woman Lake, for there was a time when it was haunted by a dangerous water nymph, or beaver woman. She had long hair, red like the fur of a beaver. Some say she abandoned the lake when the white men came, but others tell us she is still to be seen standing waist-deep in cold shallows along the irregular shore, sometimes with her whole body dabbed with red paint. All such beaver women are very beautiful, but they can be dangerous, and are known to drown people. Yet beaver women are fond of children and never allow them to be harmed; although, if given half the chance, they may well choose to keep a human child to raise as their own.

Beaver Woman Lake was later called Lake of the Jealous Women after two sisters who lived there. They married the same man and lost their loving friendship for one another. Some say it was the beaver woman who induced their jealousy by means of a spell. Others say the beaver woman left that lake because the hostilities of the two sisters were too horrible, and that the feminine apparition who is seen there now, with her dabs of red paint and enticing manner, is actually one of the jealous sisters, who became the lake's new guardian nymph.

The sisters were named Camas Flower and Marmot Woman. Camas was quiet, but Marmot was always chattering. Ever since they were small, Camas listened to her sister talk, and was glad to hear her, for Marmot was an imaginative youngster, thoroughly entertaining to the shy Camas.

So close were they that they decided they could not be parted even by marriage. Therefore they wedded the same man, who accounted himself lucky. His name was Hunts Far. Like Camas, he seldom spoke. His head was in the clouds. He scarcely noticed the strife building in his family, so he never did anything to head it off; rather, he inadvertently contributed to the divisiveness that grew from a small dark spot of unreason into a terrible shadow of obsession.

One day Marmot was cooking a meal in a basket set on hot stones. Due to an evil thought that came into her head, she dumped the stew into the firepit and said bad words. Hunts Far looked at her with amazement. He was a patient man and said, "Don't worry about spilling it, I don't mind."

"I did it on purpose!" she exclaimed. "You always favor Camas Flower! You never favor me!"

"In what way have I favored Camas over you?" he asked.

Marmot scowled and screwed up her forehead, pondering.

"Well?" said Hunts Far. "Have you thought of something?"

She said, "No I haven't, but I know you love her best."

Hunts Far shook his head and decided to go hunting, which is what he always did to avoid trouble.

~~~~~

A few days later, Hunts Far was fishing on a river and caught many fish, which he tied into a bundle. As he was heading home, he spotted two sleek dark river otters. They chased one another up and down the banks, sliding into the water and climbing out again, nipping at each other's tails. Hunts Far said, "I'll catch that one for Camas and that one for Marmot!" He crept up on them silently, awaiting his chance. Then, unleashing an arrow, he killed Camas's otter. The other slipped into the water and disappeared before another arrow was ready.

He tried the rest of the afternoon to spot the second otter. At last he decided he'd better get home with his fish and the one otter, having it in mind to find the second otter the next day. When he came to the lodge by Beaver Woman Lake, he stepped through the door and laid the otter before Camas, saying, "I caught this for you, Camas; you may have the pelt, which is strong medicine. There were two otters, so tomorrow I will catch the other one for you, Marmot."

Yet the next day Hunts Far did not go out. He had caught so very many fish the day before, he just felt like relaxing. The day after that, he set off to catch the second otter but could find no tracks, so went up into the hills to hunt goats instead.

In the meantime, Marmot was seething. While Hunts Far was away, she began to berate Camas without relent. "Our husband prefers you. Look! He gave you that otter. There you sit fixing a fine pelt, and what do I have? Nothing!"

"He's gone to get you one as well. It may be a finer pelt than this one, you never know."

"Maybe he'll bring me one, maybe he won't, but he gave you that one foremost; he thinks of you first. It's pretty clear who gets the preference around here. I can well see I'm just not wanted."

Camas winced under the continuing barrage. When she got the chance, she said softly, "You and I are twins. I have loved you always.

Even before we were born I held your hand. I love you so much and would never try to place myself first with Hunts Far, whose heart is big enough to hold us with equal caring. Cast away your bad thoughts, Marmot, my sister. When I've tanned this pelt, you may have it, as proof of my devotion."

"Did I ask for your otter pelt? I don't want it! I want our husband's consideration, that's all. But even that's too much for him. He boldly shows his favoritism!"

Nothing Camas could say gained any response beyond another harangue. So she kept still and bore it all, as Marmot persisted in thinking herself insulted and mistreated in a myriad of ways.

When Hunts Far returned without the second otter, Marmot stormed about the lodge acting cross. As each day passed, she became angrier. When Hunts Far was out, Marmot berated her sister, and when he came home yet again without an otter, she became silent and morose. Hunts Far wondered why she wasn't chattering as much as usual, but his mind was filled with so many things that he was glad of the quietude and failed to perceive it as anger.

One day Camas was digging roots when Marmot came into the woods to yell at her. "Are you industrious to show me up? Are you trying to prove you're the better wife? Our husband brings us so much meat, why dig roots? He brings us a bighorn one day, a deer the next day, and all manner of animals that live nowhere near the haunts of otters!" Having said this, she threw Camas's otter pelt on the ground, where Camas could see it had been stabbed through several times with a knife.

Camas lifted the ruined pelt with tears in her eyes. She said, "What has made you foolish, my sister? Why is it you cannot see you are dear to me? You know Hunts Far tried to find you an otter, and you could have had this one rather than cut it with holes."

"There you go pretending to be good!" Marmot said, following Camas back toward their lodge. She shouted, "We cannot live together anymore, Camas! You're a bad woman and I hate you! Come on! Get a knife and we'll fight it out! Whoever lives will be the one wife of Hunts Far."

For the first time in her life, Camas became angry. "Stupid woman!" she said. "You know I could never stab you. But I'll fight you just the same. Come on, let's swim across the lake. We'll swim back and forth until one of us is worn out and drowns. How about that? Get ready, you crazy nobody! I bet you'll sink like a rock, you've become so hard and wicked! A lake spirit will grab your legs and pull you under, just to punish you for your misguided temper!"

For a moment Marmot stood in awe of her sister's anger, which she had never before witnessed. But it was true, she had become hard as a rock. Soon she rallied her own hot emotion. "All right!" she exclaimed. "I'm ready!" She began to tear off her clothes as she ran to the shore. "I've always been stronger than you! I'll swim all day! It's you who'll drown!"

Camas ran after her, throwing her clothes off as well. They leapt into the lake and swam to the farther shore. "See, I was faster!" cried Marmot. "You're already worn out! Ha ha! Go again!"

They swam back and forth several times. Marmot was always ahead, always laughing and screaming, "You can't win, Camas! You'll drown! I'll be the one wife of Hunts Far!"

With all her shouting and pressing to stay ahead, Marmot finally wore herself out. On the last time across the lake, Camas held the lead. She could no longer hear Marmot's bad mouth. When Camas climbed onto the shore, she turned around and could not see her sister. She stood there staring in disbelief. Marmot had disappeared in the middle of the lake! There was not so much as a ripple.

With her mind lost in a daze, Camas clad herself in her buckskins and went into the lodge. She sat in a corner away from the firepit and began to cry. When Hunts Far came home late that evening, he saw Camas still weeping. "Where is Marmot?" he asked. "I caught her this otter."

Camas began to wail all the louder. She could not speak. Finally she was able to say, "She was so jealous, we had a fight. We went swimming to see who would be the first to drown."

"Can it be?" asked Hunts Far, suddenly aghast.

"Oh! The sister I so loved has drowned!"

Together they mourned as they circled and circled the lake, seeking Marmot's corpse for a proper ceremony. They never found the body.

Camas and Hunts Far were too unhappy to live by the lake anymore. They moved into the Blackfoot village some distance away. They continued to mourn for a long time; indeed, they never stopped mourning, and neither of them would ever go anywhere near that place again, that Lake of the Jealous Women.

Spirit of the Grey Wolf

An Idaho Legend of Red Fish Lake

BORN INTO THE family of a Bannock chieftain was a girl soon known as Tokti, Most Beautiful One, because of her spiritual as well as physical comeliness. Already, when she was small, the mark of future greatness was upon her.

As a child she played with the son of a hunter. They ran together upon the grassy plains, leaping and laughing. One day the boy found a bright blue feather and placed it in her hair. They gazed at one another with a startling intensity, beginning in that moment to understand what they meant to each another.

As Tokti came of age, she began to live as princesses do, in a somewhat secluded, retiring manner surrounded by maiden servants. She could no longer play with her childhood friend, as young men and young women were not free to mingle at will.

She wove from grass and wool such things as mats, blankets, banners, skirts, and adornments incorporating beads, quills, and shells, assisted by her maidens, who were skillful dyers. Everything Tokti made was a stunning work of art depicting beasts and divinities, as well as heroic portraits that somehow resembled her childhood friend. Her artworks were sought by all who had discerning taste. In Tokti's behalf, her mother traded her artistic weavings for the best quills, beads, and shells. Her banners hung in the richest tipis and lodges of tribes near and far.

Occasionally, from within the tipi, through a slit between the tightly woven mats that covered the tipi's frame, Tokti would have conversations with her childhood friend as he sat on the ground outside.

The Bannocks had known for a long while that these two youngsters were destined for one another. Yet a hunter's son could not receive a princess for his bride without first achieving wealth and fame of his own.

One day the youth set out into the plains. After he had fasted and prayed for many days, enduring hot days and cold nights, he heard, at a great distance, the howl of a grey wolf. He lifted his bow, but remained sitting on the ground in a meditative frame of mind. The sound of the wolf's howl and barking became louder by stages, until it was like thunder, by which the young hunter understood it was no common wolf that sought him.

He stood up slowly with his bow at hand. There before him was an enormous wolf with its lips peeled back, snarling and slavering. It leapt forth with jaws full wide. The young man's arrow entered the wolf's chest while it was in mid-leap, so that when the beast struck the youth and knocked him to the ground, the jaws embraced his throat, but could not clamp shut.

Quickly he skinned the wolf while it was still in its death throes, and he ate of its loins, wolf's blood painting his lips and chin. When he returned to his village, he told no one of his adventure, though they knew by his new garment that his spirit-guardian was the Grey Wolf.

He was thereafter possessed of hunting skills that exceeded natural ability, and won the name Shauntimuk, He That Brings Lots of Meat. He became prosperous by trading furs and meat for ponies, with which he intended to give the highest possible bride-price to Tokti's parents as evidence of his esteem for their daughter.

~~~~~

The day Shauntimuk chose to give the ponies to Tokti's father was selected for its auspicious character. It was late autumn, and elk and deer had been driven into the plains by snows in the mountain regions. A hunters' festival with an extravagant feast was held at Rock Creek Canyon to celebrate the abundance. Hunters came from tribes of all the surrounding regions to participate in the revelry, which included games, sports, singing, dancing, gambling, and horse racing. The gaiety continued into the depth of night, until everyone was exhausted. The next morning, the revelry was taken up anew.

The two lovers had only occasional glimpses of one another. Yet Tokti knew from their previous, furtive conversations that on the third and final day of the festival, Shauntimuk would give ponies to her parents.

Tokti's father's tipi had been moved to a central place at Rock Creek Canyon. Tokti continued to honor the tradition that unmarried princesses not display themselves overmuch. Still, as the tipi was in the middle of the festival grounds, her retiring pose was merely a polite illusion. In fact, she went forth from the tipi from time to time to participate in dances and to show herself in the wonderfully feathered and beaded garment she had created, a garment that was the epitome of her artistry and well suited to her own beauty. Her dress incorporated a great many blue, red, yellow, and white feathers that had come to her "mysteriously" over time as offerings outside her tipi. Everyone knew these feathers were choice specimens from birds and ducks taken by Shauntimuk's arrows.

On the third day of the festival, a gaunt young man arrived astride a powerful cayuse stallion. With him were many ponies and an older slave-woman who served him. From the large number of buffalo rugs upon the backs of proud ponies, it was evident that the stranger was a man of wealth. There was much speculation about him. Was he a Blackfoot? Was he a chief's son? Was he dangerous? Everyone gave way to him as he strode about the grounds. Only the children were fearless, attracted as they were by the sleekness of the stallion he led about on a tether.

The gaunt young man joined in a gambling sport that was played with small marked sticks that were moved back and forth between hands. He was very clever at this game, making it more than a game of chance. Some of the young men who were losing whispered that the stranger was a magician. The wealth of the hunters flowed swiftly into the stranger's hands.

As he would not give his name or tribe, the people called the man Itlokuna, which was the name of the gambling sport he invariably won. When he had accumulated every horse that was available, Itlokuna herded them together with his other ponies, then mounted his cayuse stallion, intending to leave.

How insulted everyone felt! This stranger had come into their midst on the last day of their festival, quickly won their horses, and then just readied himself to leave without once sharing in the fuller spirit of the gathering. Attendees began to press around Itlokuna, closing about his stallion. They insisted that he had only just arrived and there was no need to rush away. Although they were flattering and congratulatory with their words, their visages did not look pleased. When they chided Itlokuna to extend his luck in a horse race, his slave-woman whispered something to him, so that it was obvious that she was his advisor. Itlokuna agreed to stay longer and participate in the race.

Now, the Bannocks had a horse named Chinook that was greatly famed. They had never known of a horse that matched him for speed and endurance.

Chinook, the Willful Wind, was brought forth and paraded about, wearing a beaded and feathered robe created by Tokti. Itlokuna's expression became covetous of both the robe and the stallion. The Bannocks assuredly understood the excellence of Itlokuna's cayuse, but they had unwavering faith in Chinook.

The Bannocks drove a hard bargain for the wager, boasting not only of the prowess of Chinook, but also of the great value of the horse's robe, made by their gifted princess. Itlokuna waged about half the ponies he had won that day, together with his own stallion, called Sky Fire.

The stranger was a good actor. He pretended he was alarmed at having been "cornered" into wagering so much. But one man saw an evil glint in Itlokuna's eyes. Shauntimuk observed the rawboned strength of the cayuse and fretted that even Chinook would be lost because of the day's sports. Shauntimuk strode from amidst a group of hunters and said he would ride Chinook to win the race. The other young men complained that Shauntimuk had refused to participate in the day's gambling—he had taken no chances with *his* wealth—and therefore they would draw lots among themselves to see who was privileged to ride the great horse Chinook, whose dust Sky Fire would soon have in his face. Shauntimuk walked away with worried thoughts. He realized his fellows were in no mood to recognize him as their most qualified rider.

It was a close race, taking them the length of the valley and back. The two horses were often neck and neck, for they were evenly matched. But the riders were not of equal skill; the Bannock rider

Spirit of the Grey Wolf

was good, but not good enough. By a single error he gave up all hope of a lead. Chinook was defeated, and all the Bannocks were crestfallen.

Now, all this while Tokti had remained cloistered in her tipi, in part because of her disapproval of the gambling that had dominated the afternoon. When she heard Chinook would be taken away from her people, her heart sank, and she came forth in her beaded and feathered dress to say goodbye to the tribe's greatest horse. After her farewell to Chinook, she approached the other stallion to stroke the sleek fur of its neck. Despite herself, she admired Sky Fire.

When Tokti looked up at the rider, she saw a covetousness in the foxlike face gazing down upon her. She drew back from his visage with a feeling of terror.

~~~~~

Itlokuna entered a circle of old warriors who were dressed in festival garments and smoking together. He said, "Who is the father of the beautiful one?" Tokti's father nodded slightly, and Itlokuna turned to him at once. Itlokuna's slave-woman came into the circle with buffalo robes, and then she went away to get more robes, and then a third time she went for robes, and so on, until a great heap of buffalo robes had been placed in the circle of chiefs. "All these buffalo robes," Itlokuna said, "plus all the ponies I won today, and half those I came with, I give to you, Father of the Beautiful One."

"Go! Go!" said Tokti's father, with a sneer on his lips, but Itlokuna would not leave.

He said, "O Father of the Beautiful One, give me your daughter and you will become the richest of men. All my ponies I give you, keeping only three—one for myself, one for my old female attendant, and one for my new wife. Also will I send from my place in the east an equal number of ponies, doubling the number I leave for you today, and there will be many gifts and shells."

Tokti's father sat up straight and set aside his pipe. He was clearly impressed by the magnitude of the offer. Even so, he said, "Our princess cannot be given to a gambler whose tribe is unknown."

It was then that Shauntimuk came into the circle of chiefs, his wolfskin wrapped about his shoulder like the mantle of a prince. He had not expected to be in a bidding war with a gambler. The intended grandeur of Shauntimuk's moment was irretrievably lost. Nevertheless, he made his speech as he had long planned, the speech prepared in his thoughts and honed through many variations.

"My heart aches with dreams of Tokti," said Shauntimuk. "Night and day, from childhood to this minute, my heart has swollen with dreams of the beautiful one. Her heart and my heart have spoken to each another from a time before we came into this world. We recognized each other when first we began to walk. We played husband-and-wife as children, when I brought her the first rabbit that ever I hunted, and she gave me berries in a basket she had made, and which I have kept with me always."

Shauntimuk reached beneath his mantle and drew forth a little berry-stained basket woven of grass, a child's effort which even so showed the promise of Tokti's budding genius. He continued, "I have desire for Tokti. She has desire for me. Take my horses, which I have gained by honest means as a hunter with a powerful spirit. Take my wealth, all of it, but give me Tokti, and you will make two hearts glad."

All who heard were deeply moved. Even if Shauntimuk's wealth fell vastly short of what Itlokuna had offered, the choice was obvious. Surely it was the destiny of Shauntimuk and Tokti to be wed!

Itlokuna saw love for Shauntimuk upon the face of Tokti's father.

He understood that the tribe did not wish to see Tokti sent away. Before the chief could reply, Itlokuna was quick to say, "All I have offered you is many times greater than what this fellow possesses. Even so, I will give you one more thing. I will give you Sky Fire, the greatest horse that has ever lived, greater than your stallion, Chinook."

Shauntimuk was about to contradict the gambler, for he well knew he could have won the race with Chinook had he been selected as the rider. But Tokti's father raised a hand commanding silence. Many people drew close around the circle of chiefs. No one would be happy to see Tokti taken away to a distant place. Yet who could help but think of the losses of the day? Their chief could regain all the horses gambled away by the young men, plus all the ponies of Itlokuna, plus more horses that would be sent later, and other gifts as well, in addition to which there was Sky Fire, the stallion that had outrun Chinook.

Tokti's father closed his eyes and for a long time was meditative. Then he spoke: "First you will bring all the horses you have promised. Three days hence, if your words have proven true, there will be a day of feasting, and you will go away with Tokti your bride."

Then Tokti stepped into the circle in all her glory, her chin held high. In her strong, sweet voice she said, without a quiver, "Father, you have always been good to me. Your word is law." Bowing to her father's will, she conveyed none of her secret unhappiness.

〜〜〜

Shauntimuk left the valley, retiring to his hunting lodge on the plains. He lay inside the lodge, weeping with such intensity of sorrow that the sound of it was heard for miles around. His eyes swelled with redness; his nose ran until his chin was slick; his mouth was twisted into a horrible grimace. All his beauty was erased by tortured sadness.

After many hours of unceasing grief, he was transformed into a sad old man. He drew himself together sufficiently to sit up, but felt old, old. At that moment he saw, standing in the lodge, the ghostly spirit of the Grey Wolf. Shauntimuk stood up and followed the spirit-wolf out of the lodge.

For five days and nights he followed the spirit-wolf from place to place, until he was led to a beautiful lake in which dwelt vast numbers of bright red salmon. In the hills surrounding the lake dwelt many wild sheep. Shauntimuk's guiding spirit had led him to a rich and fertile place that awed his senses!

Upon the shore of the lake, the spirit-wolf stood at the side of Shauntimuk. The hunter's thoughts were so uplifted by the peace and beauty of this place that his strength and boldness were restored to him.

～～～

The absence of Shauntimuk from Tokti's marriage feast did not surprise the Bannocks, for how could he attend? Yet Tokti grieved that there had been no chance to say a farewell to the one who would be in her heart forever, even if it must be their fate never to meet again.

None could fault Itlokuna for a lack of generosity. The enormous herd of horses he provided were all perfect specimens. It had never been said how many shells and miscellaneous gifts he would give in addition to the agreed-upon horses, so when he brought innumerable baskets filled with shells and quills, the people gathered about in surprise. His old slave-woman dispersed riches among the tribe. Stone pipes with beaded or carved stems were given to the old chiefs, black obsidian to the young hunters, beads and quills to the women, and strings of shells from distant shores to leading families of the tribe. The awe-struck amazement of the Bannocks was nearly without bounds. Even so, they were sad, and all felt they had traded their hearts for shell-money, beads, and stones.

The hunters had provided deer, elk, and mountain sheep for the feast, the preparation of which was overseen by Tokti's handmaidens. Yet there was a shadow upon the feast; it might as well have been a feast of ashes. When the people looked at Itlokuna's foxlike face, they feared for the future of their princess. It seemed as though he was capable of only two expressions: covetousness and disdain.

It also appeared that Itlokuna the Gambler was older than the Bannocks had believed on his first visit. He seemed neither a young man nor an old man. There was something of each about him, and this was disconcerting.

Tokti alone was flawless. She was like the first star of morning, a bright promise, never once revealing the depth of her sadness. She was resigned to her fate, yet her resignation lay hidden in her bosom. She strove to lift up the spirits of her people. Such joy as they managed to experience on that day was due entirely to her attentive smiles.

In the midst of the feast, after Tokti's father made the marriage speech, the old slave-woman who attended Itlokuna removed the young bride from among her maidens. She said, "You will have no attendants from this day on. Follow me." Tokti followed the old woman to the buffalo-skin tipi Itlokuna had set up on the edge of the Bannock village. Only now did Tokti's strength begin to falter. She felt her knees quaking in dread of Itlokuna's touch.

Inside the tipi the old woman sat Tokti down. She said, "Do not imagine I will be a substitute for your servants. Despite appearances, I am not the gambler's slave. I am his wife, not much older than you. He is not a man, and that is why he belongs to no tribe. He is a demon who lives upon the strength of women. He will never touch you, but each time he is near, you will feel your very bones shrivel and dry. It is clear to me that you love someone or another of your tribe. Give up all hope! Even if you escape, your lover will not know you; after tonight, you will become haggard as am I. Because I am the senior wife, you will obey me in all things."

Having heard these terrible words, Tokti's stoicism fled. She covered her face with her hands and wept copious tears. The following dawn, when the Bannocks rose from their night's sleep, they saw that Itlokuna had decamped. Their princess had been taken from them without a last farewell.

~~~~~~

Itlokuna, assisted by his two wives, arranged his camp upon the high plains, with Tokti taking on the bulk of the labor under the severe hand of the older wife. When Tokti saw her reflection in a nearby spring, she was shocked to see a sallow, tired old face. It had taken Itlokuna only three days to take away her youth. He was himself rejuvenated. And Tokti realized she was indeed the slave of a demon.

Itlokuna rode upon Chinook around and around the camp. He liked the Bannock horse and did not feel he'd made a bad bargain giving up Sky Fire. He rode to where his two wives were arranging the camp and said, "I am going on ahead to a place where I know there is a Shoshone celebration. I gave up many ponies and must begin winning new ones." Then to his first wife he added, "You keep an eye on Tokti, lest she try to leave. I will beat you if she escapes, and suck out the last of your years."

When Itlokuna rode away, Tokti was glad to know he would be gone for some while. First-wife abused her all that afternoon, but Tokti bore it without complaint. That night, she collapsed inside the tipi upon a buffalo robe and felt like an old woman with a lifetime of bodily complaints. First-wife lay down on the opposite side of the tipi and, as she slept, she made sounds like a little snoring dog. Tokti watched First-wife for a while by the light of coals in the firepit. Though the old-looking woman had mistreated her, Tokti could not hate her. She felt only sorrow for First-wife, who had endured Itlokuna so much longer than had Tokti.

Unexpectedly, a wolf entered the tipi and stood near Tokti's bedding. It did not look wild but had a mild expression, like someone's pet. Then Tokti noticed the wolf was translucent. She rose from her bedding and stood by the wolf. When she looked at First-wife, who was no longer snoring, Tokti saw that the older woman's eyes were wide open. She thought First-wife would leap up and whip her back into the bed, but First-wife stared with tears in her eyes and did not move. She let Tokti follow the Grey Wolf out of the tipi and across the plains.

Tokti walked all night, following the Grey Wolf until, at the edge of the plain, they came to a box canyon in the foothills. The wolf led her to a cliff wall. At the base of the cliff stood Sky Fire, the wonderful horse that had been part of her bride-price, and beside Sky Fire was a cayuse mare smaller than Sky Fire but no less beautiful. At the mouth of a cavern partway up the cliff stood Shauntimuk, erect as a sentinel, wrapped in his famous Grey Wolf robe. He was watching the morning star as he offered prayers to the coming of the dawn. He did not rush down from his vantage point to meet Tokti. She was not surprised, for how could he recognize her, now that she was a tired old woman? She struggled to climb the slope. As Tokti approached the cave, Shauntimuk ceased singing his prayers. Tokti saw the spark of recognition enter into his eyes. Only then did he hurry to her side to assist her the rest of the way. Inside the cavern, he lay her upon a wolf-skin. He gazed at her with such extravagant affection, it was as though he could not see the furrows in her brow nor her haggard appearance.

"So soon I am old," said Tokti. "That strange gambler stole my youth and replaced it with unhappiness. Don't look at me, Shauntimuk. What can I be to you now, except a granny?"

"You are beautiful to me," said Shauntimuk, for he could see the purity and greatness in her heart. "Listen, Tokti. When you were sold for horses, I went to my hunting lodge away from the others and I wept. My sadness was so intense, my youth fled from me, and I was an old man with a face like a dried apple. Then my wolf spirit led me to a lake of red fish surrounded by hills. The peaceful beauty of the place restored me to myself. I returned to our tribe and gave all my wealth to your father in exchange for Sky Fire. Finally my wolf spirit led me to this cavern, where I have waited for you in accordance with a vision.

"The Lake of the Red Fish lies beyond the mountains, where I will take you and where we will found a nation of our own. This my vision told me. The nation we bring forth will be called People of the Clouds. From this moment on, Tokti, you must think only peaceful things. By stages you will be restored even as I was restored. Come, we can begin now, for you can see something beautiful at once!"

Tokti didn't wish to stand, for she had walked all night across the plains and was worn out. Still, she obeyed Shauntimuk. He took her to the mouth of the Cavern of the Spirit Wolf. The distant horizon was outlined by dawn's coming, red-gold heaven behind the blue-black shadows of peaks as sharp as a wolf's jaw.

Shauntimuk pointed and said, "The lake I speak of is to the south of that mountain, there."

At that moment the sun broke over the very mountain Shauntimuk indicated. The snowcapped peaks of the Sawtooth Mountains began to sparkle like a string of polished shells. As Tokti viewed the horizon in rapture, she felt the aching weariness pass from her bones. She exclaimed at the vision before her, "Ah'da'ho!" which means "Beautiful Sunlight Breaking On The Mountains." Shauntimuk replied softly to her, "See, already your premature old age begins to fade," and he embraced her tightly.

~~~~~~

As they rode side by side in the direction of the Sawtooths, how could Tokti help but think beautiful thoughts, seeing Shauntimuk all the time? When they had gone half the distance to Red Fish Lake, already she was halfway restored to her youth. The riding lovers sang songs of gratitude to the Grey Wolf and the Great Spirit. Whenever they camped beside pools or springs, they would pray by their camp-fire, and after praying they teased one another in various loving ways, so that laughter filled the night sky.

When they were on the last leg of their journey, Tokti was almost entirely her old self. It remained only to see the lake to complete her restoration.

As they broke camp that last morning, they were interrupted by the sound of the grass parting. Itlokuna leapt forth to confront them. Soon his old-looking wife appeared behind him, her face battered and bruised. She had been beaten for letting Tokti escape.

Itlokuna was a gambler, not a warrior. When Shauntimuk took a powerful posture against him, the gambler backed away. He had a cunning smile. "Listen, hunter, you have my wife, for whom I paid dearly. Even so, I know her heart is not mine, so I will be generous. I will make you a wager, and you can win her from me. What do you say? You have a mare and Sky Fire. Throw in that childish basket you carry at your belt! Wager them against Tokti, and if you win the bet, you'll have her honestly, and not as a thief who steals wives."

"No, Shauntimuk," Tokti whispered. "Itlokuna is a demon who wins by fraud."

Shauntimuk said to her, "He is right, though; I would be a thief and a murderer if I killed him in a fight. What can I do but gamble?"

Tokti said, "If it must be so, make the wager sweeter. Say you want First-wife for your servant; then we can set her free if you win. Say you want Chinook if he loses."

"Let it be so," said Itlokuna, hearing Tokti's additions to the bet. "What game shall we play?"

"Not a game, a race. I'll ride Sky Fire, and you Chinook."

Itlokuna laughed. "Good! You have made the bargain yourself! Remember it! Ha ha! You think that because Sky Fire beat Chinook before, he will do it again. Ignorant fellow! I would have lost that race to Chinook but that the rider made him stumble. So I am ready! Let's go to the base of the mountain and then back here to your camp!" Without further preamble, Itlokuna kicked Chinook and was away like the wind. Shauntimuk raced after him toward the far mountain. Tokti and First-wife clung to each other as they observed the swift horses. Tokti whispered, "Do you see it?"

"Yes, I see," said First-wife. "How strange! There is a wolf running alongside Sky Fire."

"It is not so strange," said Tokti. "It is my lover's spirit-wolf. Look there! It has veered aside into tall grass and disappeared."

~~~~~

Now, the fact was that Chinook and Sky Fire were equal in every respect, and Shauntimuk knew it. Itlokuna had gained a lead because of his cheating start, and Shauntimuk could not hope to overcome him unless the gambler made an error. If both men rode flawlessly, they would go the whole race with the same distance between them.

Although Shauntimuk had to admit his rival was a skillful rider, Itlokuna had a fatal flaw: his vanity was such that he could not recognize excellence in another. It was vanity that made him first shout a boast into the air and then look back in order to yell an insult at Shauntimuk. That was the error that allowed Sky Fire to come neck-and-neck with Chinook.

They raced to the base of the mountain without either horse gaining or losing distance. The two stallions reared up and turned about together at the exact moment, and began back toward the starting point. The eyes of Shauntimuk's steed were blazing with eagerness to win, while Chinook, a horse whose very soul was pride, snorted gales as he fought to defeat the cayuse.

Itlokuna whipped Chinook with a cord until his haunches bled, but it was not the beating that made Chinook fight to win. Then the gambler unexpectedly whipped the cord across Shauntimuk's shoulder. It stung fiercely, but Shauntimuk made no error that would throw off Sky Fire's splendid timing. Again and again the cord struck Shauntimuk's shoulder and face, yet he dared not alter Sky Fire's headlong rush, or Chinook would win an advantage.

The finish line was near. Sweat fell like rain off Chinook's neck. Steam evaporated off the neck and flanks of Sky Fire. It looked as though the two stallions would reach their destination without a winner, so that after all nothing would be settled.

Suddenly, Itlokuna gave a frightened shout. A snarling grey wolf leapt up from the tall grass, its slavering jaws glinting with sharp teeth. The gambler drew back the reins, breaking Chinook's swift stride with such a sudden jerk that the stallion reared and threw Itlokuna to the ground. In that instant, the wolf vanished as though it had not been real.

Shauntimuk rode alone into the camp. He dismounted and took Tokti in his arms. As they hugged, they heard First-wife cry out, for Itlokuna was running at them from the grass with an expression of hatred on his face and a hatchet held above his head. Shauntimuk threw Tokti from the path of Itlokuna's onslaught, drew a knife from the sheath at his belt, and blocked the downward blow of Itlokuna's hatchet.

Shauntimuk's knife sheared through the wooden handle of the hatchet so that its head was flung away, and Itlokuna was left holding a useless stick. Shauntimuk tripped the gambler to the ground, placing his foot on Itlokuna's hand until it opened and dropped the hatchet handle. Then Shauntimuk bent down and twice drew the knife across the palm of the gambler's hand, slicing two deep cuts in the form of an X.

As he stepped away, Shauntimuk let Itlokuna stand. He said, "From this day on, you have a name: Bloody Hand. Well I know that you will bring trouble everywhere you go, and I should kill you for the peace of the land. But you are marked, so people will know you. Thus I set you free." And Bloody Hand stumbled away over the plains.

In the aftermath, Tokti and Shauntimuk were briefly reunited with their tribe. Shauntimuk traded Chinook for many cayuse mares, so the stallion was restored to the Bannocks, bringing Shauntimuk a hero's fame.

First-wife had traveled with the lovers. In the light of their great love, she was partially restored to her former youth. Tokti's family offered to adopt First-wife, and she was amenable. Shauntimuk said, "First she must come with Tokti and me to the Lake of the Red Fish, the sight of which will erase the last of the evil that has harmed her. Then First-wife will return to live among the Bannocks, although Tokti and I will not return."

The tribe Tokti and Shauntimuk founded at Red Fish Lake was in later years called the Sheepeater tribe by the whites, though they called themselves the People of the Clouds. Somewhere near the lake, in a secret place, is the burial site of Tokti and Shauntimuk, whose spirits are still to be seen, in a small touring canoe, in the mists of the haunted lake.

The Mysterious Hermit of Little Falls
A Story of Falls Creek and the St. Joe River

》》》

IT MUST HAVE been about 1977, give or take a year, when I was still a relative newlywed, that my wife, Janey, and myself set off on a daylong hiking tour in the Bitterroot Mountains of northern Idaho. We hiked six miles from a quiet town, following the St. Joe River until we came to Little Falls, where Falls Creek plunges into the St. Joe. It was such a lovely spot, despite the removal of many of the trees, that we lingered in that restful place.

The wide, squat falls was pleasingly noisy rolling off the hill. A nearby meadow was ablaze with wildflowers, with far more varieties than was altogether natural to find in one place. We detected a loving hand at this labor; because many of the bushes were quite old, it seemed as though someone must have been seeding the meadow for decades rather than years.

In the field I found a fallen post with sign affixed. I flipped over the rotted lumber to see what the sign said. It was mostly eaten away by worms, yet in the surviving flakes of red and white paint I could make out the remnant of a hand-printed notice, "Flowers And Bugs Love Their Lives—Do Not Harm Them." We had a mild laugh about that and tried to prop up the crumbling sign where others could see it too.

We went out amidst the grass to admire the density of blossoms.

It was a veritable Eden. At the sight of a deep-blue flower unlike anything either of us had ever seen, Janey exclaimed, "Oh, Jason! I simply must have this for our window box! There are some small shoots starting up along here. I know we shouldn't, but let's take just one of the smaller plants with a bit of its soil."

She took a small folding firepit shovel from my pack, intending to dig up the smallest of the bushes surrounding the mother plant. She had the idea in mind, I did not doubt, that I would carry it about for her the rest of the day. However, before she could stab the soil with the shovel, an old man came upon us as if from nowhere and said, "You mustn't harm the flowers, or the insects for that matter, or anything else."

Janey leapt away from the blue flower. She was chagrined and nonplussed, for she well knew she'd been on the verge of breaking a law. The old man was densely bearded, but his beard had been tightly braided and was tucked inside his shirt. He wore a long-tailed coat in tattered condition, threadbare trousers, and worn-out shoes with lengths of leather gimp knotted about them to hold them together. For all the poverty of his garments, the oldster was exceedingly neat and clean.

Never have I met a man who seemed more harmless than this eccentric woodsman. Anyone would have welcomed him as a grandfather. Yet Janey stammered due to her embarrassment at being caught trying to steal a plant. She said, "I—I—I'd take good care of it at home . . . I meant no harm, really, I . . ."

"Look here," I interrupted, standing up for my wife. "What's a little bush more or less, when there are so many?"

The old man reached into a vest pocket and then held out his hand to Janey. He said, "Take these seeds. I gathered them last year from that very bush. You'll find them quite hardy if you never let them dry out completely."

"Oh!" she said delightedly. "Thank you! I *will* cherish them, truly!"

Then turning to wander away, he waved his hand back at us as he called out, "Don't hurt living things!"

Then very curiously, we lost sight of him due to sunlight gleaming off the falls. He seemed actually to vanish!

After Janey wrapped the seeds in a handkerchief, we explored Little Falls, where we found the remnant of a log cabin with its roof caved in. Near the cabin we spied a heap of rocks that may have been a nameless grave. Then we stumbled upon a half-fallen-away trail carved in the side of the hill that led to a stunning little grotto with overhanging ferns.

There'd once been a picnic table in the grotto, but all that remained of it was a rotted pair of crossed table legs pinned with rusty nails. "Isn't this is a perfect spot, Janey? Look, here's a firepit that needs only a little shoveling. Why don't we just have a fire?"

Janey laid a blanket on the ground as I began to unpack our repast and utensils. The peaceful solitude was so soothing, we felt at that moment we could be happy as the last man and woman on earth.

~~~~~

Early in the evening we hiked back into town, where we had a room at a bed-and-breakfast. After we cleaned up and put on fresh clothing, we strolled to a quaint restaurant on the main floor of a Victorian house. The restaurant was run by an elderly couple who lived upstairs.

Old Mrs. Kolvern was our waitress; her husband was the restaurant's chef. The fare was what I'd call "inland Italian," which in no way resembled anything from Italy, but was an extraordinarily good

Scandinavian imitation. Mr. Kolvern could have been a leading, innovative chef anywhere in the world. It was thrilling to find such fine cuisine in a small Idaho town.

Mrs. Kolvern was extremely friendly, inquiring as to how we were enjoying our stay in the valley.

"It's been great," I said. "It's beautiful country for hikers."

Janey added, "Today I best liked meeting a sweet old hermit near Little Falls, though I must say your husband's cooking is a close second when it comes to wonderful things."

"The hermit?" Mrs. Kolvern inquired, her expression suddenly ashen. Then she called to her husband. "Neil! Neil, come out here a minute."

Mr. Kolvern came out of the kitchen in his apron, wiping his hands on a clean towel. "What's the emergency?" he asked.

"They saw the hermit," his wife replied.

Neil Kolvern's handsomely wrinkled brow rose sharply as he looked at us with a quizzical intensity. "Who told you about the hermit?" he asked.

"Why, no one," I said, vaguely alarmed by the sudden change of mood. "We just met him is all. He gave my wife some wildflower seeds."

As Mrs. Kolvern trundled away to wait another table, she said to her husband, "You just take a moment, Neil, and tell them about him."

He spun a chair about from an empty table and sat near us. He began, "The hermit came to the St. Joe Valley before the big fire of 1910, when he was already middle-aged. I remember him from when I was a young man, though not many others will recall him anymore."

"Middle aged before 1910?" I asked, incredulous. "Are you saying we saw a ghost?"

"You wouldn't be the first," said the chef, and his paternal smile was reassuring. He continued, "No one knew where he came from or why he lived such a furtive, secluded life. He may have had a sordid past, but he was never the least trouble around here. He was well liked. He built a cabin by Little Falls, where he tended a field of wildflowers with the intensity of a monk performing some lifelong expiation. He placed signs everywhere, with slogans like 'Don't Kill Insects Or Any Living Thing' and 'Enjoy Your Campsite But Do Not Hurt Bushes.' He cut a stony path from the hillside leading to the falls, and built a picnic table with benches in a small grotto. It's all gone to rot by now, I suppose.

"Many people knew him in between the wars, as he had created a wonderful camping site that was often visited by valley residents on outings. He owned a small boat in which he gave visitors rides below the falls. I remember my mother riding about in her white dress, holding a parasol against the sun, as the hermit pushed with a long pole to position the boat just so in order to provide the nicest views.

"He was rarely seen in town. Not once did he ever receive or send a single letter. He must have been eighty or ninety years old when after forty years in the valley he was found dead in his cabin. He'd pinned a note to his shirt that said simply, 'Bury me in my beloved valley.' His grave is near the falls, where, as you have been privileged to discover, he still enjoys the thunder of the plunging waters. There is no name on his grave, for he never told anyone what it was."

I have always been disinclined to believe wild tales, though I long remembered and appreciated the story Janey and I heard on our first trip to the St. Joe Valley. That old man we met at Little Falls could have been anyone, and need not have been the ghost of a hermit who was even then more than thirty years dead.

The Mysterious Hermit of Little Falls

Janey, more sensitive than I, was inclined to believe. She planted the precious seeds in a window box where they flourished. When we bought our own home in Spokane, she transplanted the flowers to the garden. They still bloom generously every year, looking like tiny blue roses, without thorns, their subtle odor inspiring dreamy rumination. No one of our acquaintance has ever been able to give us the name of this charming wildflower, so we have always called it the Hermit Rose. Janey is careful of the seeds, and shares them with anyone who is touched with admiration for wild, mysterious beauty.

The Shinbone Staff

A Legend of the Necanicum River

IN THE DARK, in the dismal dark, in the dread and dismal dark, a Seatco went striding north along the shore of the open ocean, going in the direction of the nation of Clatsop. The tide was out, and lapped quietly at the flat beach. The Seatco took long loping strides over the wet sand and across barnacled rocks.

Now, this Seatco was like a man, but taller than men are ever apt to be. He was so gaunt that his ribcage showed through the holes in his ragged robe woven from sedge and strips of sinew. He bore a walking staff made of human shinbones, loosely bound together with tendons so that the bones knocked against one another every time the butt struck the ground. The sound was like that of a skeleton dancing over rocks.

There was no moon that night. The sky was lightly overcast and only one star winked in the sky, like the eye of an evil divinity. The Seatco strode along with an uneven gait and came to a small cove protected by a jetty of sand on the north side of Tillamook Head. Above the tide line was a cedar-thatch hut. Outside the hut was an old dugout with a salmon carved on one side. A large fishnet was strung across braces and poles to dry. There was also a small dip net and three barbed fishing spears.

The Seatco raised his shinbone staff and rattled it against the door of the hut.

A Clatsop Indian opened the door. His eyes at once grew round. He was a bachelor and lived apart from his tribe with only a faithful dog called Kwah. The Indian was named Fishing Lynx, because he was a good fisherman, a loner like a lynx, and had little tufts of hair growing on the tops of his ears. Fishing Lynx told Kwah to stop growling, though he himself shared the dog's mistrust of the Seatco. It would not do to be unfriendly to such a being, or the terrible visitor might tear him apart instantly.

The Seatco said, "I am an ascetic among my kind. Though I am used to cold and hunger, even so, it is damp out here tonight. I would beg of you a morsel of salmon and a shadowy corner of your hut in which to take shelter until tomorrow night."

Fishing Lynx tried to wear a welcoming expression and strove to convey curiosity rather than dread. He was a short, stout man clad in a sleeveless deerskin shirt and sealskin apron. His upper arms had sooty tattoos. He was very strong in the shoulders and arms, yet he did not welcome a wrestling match with a Seatco.

Fishing Lynx hoped friendliness would save him, so he said, "It is rare that your kind speaks to mine. Please, please come in. It is a great honor to meet a holy ascetic among the Seatco. Yes, I have salmon freshly caught today, and a bit of cake made of mortared root and berries."

The gaunt monster leaned down low in order to fit through the door of the hut. He sat on the dirt floor, as he was too tall to stand within. He laid the shinbone staff across his knees, and the nature of that staff did not go unnoticed by Fishing Lynx. Here and there the bones were carved with hideous little faces and miniature demonic figures with their knees raised high in leaps and crazy dances.

The inside of the hut was barely lit by the orange coals of a nearly smokeless firepit. Fishing Lynx did not like the way the light played off the grey sunken cheeks of his guest. It was not possible in the dim light to tell whether or not the Seatco had eyes. The fisherman prepared the fish and the root-and-berry cake for his visitor, who received and ate this repast without thanks or enthusiasm.

As he prepared a shadowy corner for the Seatco's rest, Fishing Lynx whispered to Kwah, "I am not glad to have this visitor, but you and I must be good hosts. These ghouls have been known to eat people. With luck, that fish and rootcake has sated his appetite."

The Seatco had all this while watched his host with sullen gaze. After Fishing Lynx laid out a grass mat, the Seatco feigned weariness (for Seatco do not really sleep by night). He crawled upon bony knees into the dark corner. Refusing the offer of a blanket, and covered only in his ragged robe, the Seatco lay curled on his side, his back against the wall. He became so motionless Fishing Lynx supposed the monster really was sleeping.

Fishing Lynx thought he had better stay awake all night, but he had worked a long day of fishing with no helper but Kwah, and he feared he might easily fall asleep in spite of the danger. As the firepit coals had ceased to be smoky, the fisherman reached up to the ceiling and unpropped the smoke-hole cover, closing it in order to hold the last warm0th in the hut. Then he lay down on a bed of furs and covered himself with an old bearskin. Kwah lay nearby, guarding his master, worried eyes fixed on the lightless corner across the room.

The Seatco gave a low, menacing chuckle. He murmured to himself, "Look at that Clatsop man already snoring. What a stupid fellow! And his dog is stupid, too. As soon as the dog goes to sleep, I'll have a *good* meal out of that man."

The Shinbone Staff

But Fishing Lynx's snoring was pretended. He heard the Seatco's fearful plan and became greatly distraught. When the coals died out completely, it was not possible to see a thing, and even a Seatco needed at least one star to see by. Fishing Lynx crawled quietly from under his blanket and put a cedar board in his place. He crept to the farthest corner of his hut from where the Seatco lay. Two days previous, Kwah had been digging in that corner, and Fishing Lynx had scolded him for doing so. But now he was glad. He moved the loose earth from that corner, uncovering a hole large enough that he might escape under the wall.

Then, placing a hand on the head of Kwah in the dark, he whispered very softly, so that only the sharp ears of a dog could hear. "Kwah, will you give your life for mine? If you will, and if I survive, I'll remember you in the story that will afterward be told. Oh, poor Kwah, how sorry I am I chastised you for digging in this corner. Are you a prophet-dog and knew I would need it? Listen, I will escape to the ferryman at Necanicum River and take refuge in my people's nation. Will you lay yourself on top of this hole so the Seatco cannot see my route and deduce which direction I have fled? If you love me, lay yourself over the hole when I am gone, and try your best not to give me away."

Only moments after Fishing Lynx was gone, the gaunt monster pounced through the darkness, lunged upon the bearskin blanket, and snatched for his intended feast. But all he caught hold of was a cedar board. His bony fingers clutched the wood so harshly he left impressions, creating the appearance of ribcage. Throwing the board aside, he tossed open the hide-hinged door of the hut and gazed into the damp, cool night.

He could not see any track in the sand. His ears were attuned to the night, but he could hear only the rushing of the waves and small crabs skittering over kelp-draped stones. He decided the Clatsop man must still be hiding in the hut. He crawled toward the hut's only bench and yanked out old blankets, baskets of dried fish, boxes of utensils, and other objects from under it, scattering everything around the floor. Then he stood straight up and threw open the smoke-hole, poking his head through it, but he found no one on the roof.

There was nowhere else the Clatsop could have hidden. By the light of the one star through the open smoke-hole, the Seatco saw Kwah lying in the far corner. He commanded, "You! Disgusting dog! Which way did your master run?"

The dog pointed his nose toward the door, the opposite direction from the Necanicum River. He woofed, "Ya Wah!" which in the language of the Clatsops means, "That way!"

Immediately the Seatco flew out the door and ran along the beach, peering left and right for signs of the man's trail in the sand.

The monster ran a great distance south from Tillamook Head without seeing any footprints but those he himself had made earlier in the night. He leapt over Elk Creek, and only when he saw the scowling face of the God of Mount Neahkahnie did he slow his remarkable pace, realizing he'd been misled. A deep anger arose within his dried-out heart as he thought how easily the dog fooled him.

He rushed back to the hut and found the hated dog still lying over the hole. The Seatco shouted, "Lying dog!" Then he touched Kwah with the shinbone staff. Sad to say, Kwah did not have even sufficient time to whimper. He shriveled away into dust and, lo! the hole by which Fishing Lynx escaped was revealed.

Now the Seatco saw where the fisherman had fled along a trail into the woods away from the beach. He loped at full pace after his prey. The high trail went along a ridge and led to the place overlooking where the Necanicum River spills into the sea. From there, the fisherman's track turned inland along the river.

Soon the Seatco spied the ferryman called Kon-wahk-shoo-ma, "Old Man Thunder."

"Has a Clatsop man passed here?" the Seatco demanded gruffly.

"I have shuttled him across the river," said Old Man Thunder in a deep, rumbling voice.

Now, Old Man Thunder's method of ferrying people was quite odd. He had the power to stretch forth his foot to form a bridge. Old Man Thunder said, "I will stretch forth my foot for you, but you must first swear not to touch me with your shinbone staff. For I am a purified one, an immortal god, and wish not to be polluted by the touch of death."

"I will not touch you with my staff," swore the Seatco.

Old Man Thunder's foot began to stretch forth and widen to form a bridge. The Seatco ran halfway across the span. He spotted Fishing Lynx by the light of the single star! So excited was he by the sight of his meal, he forgot his promise, and placed his bone staff on the bridge.

The purified one immediately felt defiled. He withdrew his foot, and the Seatco plunged into the water far below. The current was terrible at that season, and swept the Seatco away. Old Man Thunder said with a rumbling, disdainful voice, "Pass into the ocean, evil one, and be transformed into the surf."

Thereafter the Seatco haunted the sea, and that is why the tides are cruel along those shores. Yet no matter how violently the surf struck the beaches, the Seatco never again walked upon that land.

The Woman Whose Husband Was a Seal
A Legend of Coos Bay

A YOUNG MAIDEN lived near the northern sandbar of Coos Bay. She was a great swimmer. No matter what the weather, she liked to swim—in sunlight, in rain, during storms. This remarkable woman gathered shellfish even at high tide, dipping and sliding in the water. Someone once said, "That girl's practically an otter," after which she was called by the name Sea Otter Maiden.

One day Sea Otter Maiden didn't return from swimming. She wasn't seen for more than two moons. Her parents grieved, wailing, "She is lost! She is lost!" Then they were informed that their daughter had been seen living among the seals. Whenever the seals were sunning themselves on a rock out in the ocean, the young woman was among them, wearing five sea-otter skins. Sometimes she would be standing upright. Sometimes she lounged amidst them in the attitude of a seal. Whenever the seals saw people approaching, they fled into the ocean, and Sea Otter Maiden went with them.

Her mother and father went to the end of the bar to see the seal rock. They called and called, but their daughter ignored them. With supporters, they set out with three canoes to capture her. It was not so easy. Over and over, day after day, she evaded them.

"We cannot seize her," her father said. Once he had been a famous seal hunter, but now he could not capture his own daughter. He said to his wife, "It is doubtful we will ever catch her."

Then one day a group of seals was lounging on the sandy shore near the mouth of the Coos River. Sea Otter Maiden's mother and father saw her with the seals and ran after her with a net. The seals scooted swiftly toward the sea. The young woman ran with them, but she stumbled and fell. The net wrapped about her. Kicking and barking in the manner of her adopted clan, she was forced to return to her old home.

Her family watched her night and day, lest she go back into the sea. At first she would not talk, but only barked, and would not eat salmon if it was cooked. Slowly she returned to her old self, but with such a melancholy look that her family worried.

One evening she was sitting in her family's lodge. Salmon hung drying from the ceiling amidst smoke from the firepit. Her mother's sweet-scented herbs hung from a crossbeam in baskets.

Sea Otter Maiden was gazing upward through the smoke-hole. She could see the stars. They were like campfires of distant villages viewed from the bottom of a sea. Her family watched her with muted expectation. Then, still watching the stars through the smoke-hole, she began to speak dreamily. She told them how she came to be living among the seals.

~~~~~

I was swimming in the bay (the young woman began). I saw a beautiful man standing at the tip of the bar. I had never seen him before, but I was not alarmed, for his face expressed kindness and amusement. He was clad in a sealskin and had a whalebone knife through his belt. His leggings were decorated with beads and he wore a headdress of cormorant feathers.

He asked me, "Why do you swim all the time?" He spoke just like someone from our village.

"I am hunting for food," I replied. I showed him a large clam. He watched me as though he thought I was funny. So I laughed back at him, splashing as I swam away.

He called after me, "The way you swim, you belong to the sea." I was flattered. He continued, "You will be my wife! Come with me to my home, and you will have all kinds of food."

This he said to me, and I found my heart was willing. He entered the water and began to walk out into the sea. I swam next to him and asked, "Won't people look for me and worry?"

"You will always be nearby," he said. "They will see you with my people when we are sunning on the rocks. We two will go deep into the water. Here, take hold of my belt."

"Won't I lose my breath?"

"You must close your eyes as we go down. When I tell you to look, then you may open your eyes." I closed my eyes until we came to a big lodge in a village at the bottom of the ocean. I met my husband's family. They are people like the Coos. Only when they come to the top of the ocean do they look like seals.

I visited each house of their village as my husband made introductions. It seemed to me as though I was not in the water. Everyone was friendly as they went about their business performing ordinary daily chores. When the Coos find empty clamshells along the beach, it is because they were cleaned by the women in the underwater village.

Some of their houses are made of sand inlaid with seashells. Some are hollow rocks with kelp across the doors. My husband is the chief's son. Oh! I miss my husband. I weep!

~~~~~

On quiet evenings, Sea Otter Maiden told other tales of her life below the waves. She sounded as though she thought the seals had a better village than her own. Sometimes she closed her eyes and listened to things in the sea that no one else could hear. Because she possessed such a tragic countenance, all who looked at her felt sad as well.

One day no one could find her. The villagers feared she had returned to the sea, until someone heard her weeping and followed the sound. She sat on the ground amidst lacy ferns on the north shore of the South Coos River in a little grotto under a cliff. Droplets of water fell from the mosses on the cliff wall, mingling with the tears on the young woman's face, so that forever after that place was called Maiden Tears Grotto.

After that scare, the chief and the subchief came to Sea Otter Maiden's family lodge early in the evening to instruct her never to go swimming again, for she might be tempted to leave her people. This was a painful instruction for her to receive, for she had loved the water even in infancy, and swam before she walked. It was painful to bow to the will of the chiefs, but she was respectful, and strove toward obedience.

Whenever she was near the beach, seals would come and call to her. She would answer them, calling each by a name. Though her family watched her closely, one day while everyone was gathering shellfish, she slipped away. They looked for her the whole day, but found only her footprints leading into the sea.

She was unseen for many months, for she well knew her family would try to catch her if she showed herself. Her mother went to the bar each day and called. Never was there an answer. The mother consulted a tribal doctor, who eased her grief when he said, "She has become our people's guardian spirit. As intermediary between the seal people and the Coos, she is now divine, protecting our fishermen and seal hunters from the dangers of the ocean."

One day Sea Otter Maiden's father was out in a canoe beyond Coos Bay. He saw his daughter in the shallows near a marsh. With her were two baby seals who swam around her. They poked their sweet faces out of the water, gazing on her with their large black eyes. They spoke to her with endearing puppy sounds.

Her father cried out, "My child! My child! Hello! I've been fishing here."

"My father!" said the woman, looking toward the canoe. "As you see, I have two children. I miss you sometimes. I miss my mother. But now I live in the sea. I want to come and visit you one more time. You must promise not to detain me, for the sake of my children."

Her father paddled home and told his wife. A few days later, they prepared a great feast of clams, salmon, and elk, as well as roots of camas, fern, and skunk cabbage. The village gathered around the lodge of Sea Otter Maiden's family, for all wished to greet her. Then she came to visit her family for the last time. She brought many sea-otter pelts and shell-money. She said, "This is the marriage-price from my husband. He could not come himself."

There was a celebration that ran late into the night. They called it a wedding party, though the groom was absent. Sea Otter Maiden was deeply moved. She held each member of her family close, one after the other. At last she said, "Now I must return to my new home. You will not see me again, but do not grieve. They are like people, and my husband is a great prince who will one day become chief."

Then she strode out into Coos Bay, where the greenly shimmering waves were lit by moon and stars. Not once did she turn to look back. She dove down, and was gone.

The Woman Whose Husband Was a Seal

From time to time, her family saw Sea Otter Maiden out on the rocks, playing with her children. A big seal was sometimes near her, broad chested, with a deep, proud bark. When the sun was just right, the Coos people could see the village under the sea, made of rocks and sand.

The Wild Voyage of the Steamship *Dora*
A Tale of the North Pacific Coast

⌇

THE STEAMSHIP *DORA* was condemned in the 1920s, when she was set afire on Richmond Beach, Alaska. As ships are known to have souls, hers assuredly went upward into the clouds, carried upon smoke and ashes.

A few old hands were in attendance, with long faces and hats in hands, to bid the old vessel a last farewell. There was but one newspaper reporter to record the event, eager to remind the public of the ship's strange and spirited history.

~~~~~

She'd been built as a whaler, and her first home port was in Puget Sound. In days when the *Dora* was young and mounted with harpoons, many a bloody geiser flowered from the blowholes of wounded whales during her journeys to frigid northern seas under low, glowering skies, or west to Hawaii and Japan and the waters of China.

In 1909 her far travels ceased. To her embarrassment and chagrin, she was refitted to carry mail and passengers for the Alaska Steamship Lines, for whom she plied a supply route from Seward to Kodiak, hugging the coastline like some cowardly old woman forever ready to run for the shelter of cove or port.

This was her unlucky fate for several years until, at last, she grew bored and rebellious over so tame and demeaning a life. At least, that's what old salts claimed afterward, for no sailor has ever doubted ships have intentions of their own, and a whaler accustomed to the high seas is apt to feel it an acute insult to discover herself fallen to the sedate tasks of a coastal mail carrier.

While the *Dora* was anchored off Cold Bay, Alaska, waiting for a thick fog to lift, a storm rose unexpectedly from the sea and ripped her from her anchor. As she made her eager break for the high seas, the crew hurried to lower another anchor. No sooner had the anchor grabbed the seabed than it, too, was broken from its chain. Now the crew was in a flustered panic. One bumbling error led to another. The third anchor, rarely used, turned out not to be properly attached, and it took a full length of chain with it to the ocean floor.

Though the winds slowly lifted the fog, a slating rain kept visibility as bad as ever. The storm carried the ship across the Gulf of Alaska and out into the Pacific, far from Alaskan shores. "Oh!" thrilled the soul of the *Dora*. "Freedom!" She was leading a high wave, and there was no turning her back.

With passengers and crew, there was a total of twenty-one men and one woman on board. At first the passengers heard only excuses about delays in returning to Cold Bay and thence to other ports along the coast. But after the ship had wandered several days, it became all too clear that something was amiss. Finally the cook, a man named Thomas Wilson, let the cat out of the bag one evening while dinner was being served. He mentioned for all to hear that the *Dora*'s compass had failed. Her present course was unknown and, as the navigator had failed to find shore or port, the ship's fuel was nearly spent.

The nervous look upon Thomas's face was not reassuring. When several of the passengers found themselves unable to eat in their state of worry, Thomas was careful to save what was left over, aware that the small store of food must be stretched to the maximum. Soon indeed the ship would be without fuel, with few supplies, and aimlessly adrift.

Well before thirty days had elapsed, it had become evident to the captain and crew that the old whaling ship was visiting her personally favored haunts of better days. The crew had first spotted the Hawaiian Islands when hardly two weeks lost, and had made an effort to hail another steamer, which passed at too great a distance to realize the *Dora* was adrift. Before another two weeks passed, they twice passed near whalers' ports in China, but could do nothing to help themselves since the fuel was long spent. Ports came into view, but just as it seemed inevitable to the crew that they must momentarily encounter a ship close enough to hear their cry for salvation, the *Dora* turned her prow about, as with a stubborn volition, and let land sink once more below the horizon.

Off the Japanese coast, which she had often visited in her youthful days, she became trapped by a small reef. Twisted left and right, it seemed she might well be torn apart, taking the twenty-two on board to the bottom of the sea, their bones and her braces to become encrusted corals, and no one in the world would have known their fate. But after several hours of hard pounding, a wave washed her free. She was yet again adrift on the high seas in search of beloved places.

The supply of water was nearly exhausted. During squalls, everything that could hold rainfall was put out. Tarps were arranged to catch more water, which ran into pots and jars and wooden barrels. These efforts proved barely sufficient to keep passengers and crew from dehydration and madness. So, too, they wiled away dull, helpless days of voyaging by fishing over the sides, for otherwise all would have starved.

The Wild Voyage of the Steamship Dora

At the end of two months of wandering the Pacific, Thomas was washed overboard in a storm. Despite efforts to save him, he was seen no more; and in the sunlight of a calmer day, the captain held a touching service on deck, and tears streaked the cheeks of hardened men. More than one pondered and fretted how, with the next storm, their own fates might prove no better than poor Tom's.

With the loss of Thomas, the low spirits on board the *Dora* plunged to still greater depths. Although there were no more storms, a pall nevertheless hovered about the mood of the passengers and crew. A fistfight erupted over the honor of the woman passenger. There were outbursts of hysterics by sailors who had reached their limit, strong men whose strength availed them nothing without fuel or compass. The captain had all hands cleaning the ship, in an attempt to maintain decorum and restore spirits, but his efforts backfired and there was a mild revolt. A momentary and irrational threat of mutiny was only halted when the two half-mad instigators came to their senses, realized they were helpless in any case, and fell into the captain's arms in an emotional outburst of apologetic sorrow.

None believed they should ever see land again, except in the teasing way the *Dora* had shown them the coasts of China and Japan. They were convinced they would become a collection of corpses on a rusting bucket, a deathship wandering like the *Flying Dutchman* until the end of time.

Yet the *Dora* truly was in full possession of her wits. She had by this time seen all the places she had longed to see one last time before settling into a mail ship's retiring ways. After ninety-two days, she had revisited all those parts of the ocean that had once been dear to her. Now it was time to return her passengers to the first of her home ports.

One night the captain, unable to sleep, returned to the pilot-house. Through a parting of the fog that seemed the ship's eternal companion, he spotted a light in the dark distance. He thought he recognized that steady white light, but dared not hope it really was the Tatoosh Island lighthouse. Upon the dawn, he saw that indeed that they were approaching the Strait of Juan de Fuca, and Cape Flattery was dead ahead. As the passengers awoke and came on deck, each observed the famous light, and hope found renewal in their bosoms.

If there had ever been any doubt until then that the *Dora* had known her way all along, there could be none now. She was returning to her original home port in Puget Sound as surely as a homing pigeon returns to roost in the place where it was born. The only problem now would be getting past Cape Flattery, which was treacherous. As the inrushing tide sucked the *Dora* into the Strait, her chance of drifting by Duncan Rock in safety were one in a thousand.

The passengers and crew scarcely dared hope for another miracle. Without power or tug escort, they must inevitably be lost upon the rocks, taken into the cold eternal sea a scant hour from safe harbor.

"All hands!" cried the captain, and passengers as well as crew hearkened the call. "Gather up everything that burns and take it to the boiler room! That means the cabins, the chairs, wooden cabinets, doors, trunks, even your shoes! Everything! We'll put power back into this girl and limp home with her yet!"

Axes and crowbars were dispersed among all. Even the one woman on board hiked up her skirt and tore into the walls of a cabin, axe in hand, with a lumberjack's ferocity. Every piece of furniture was chopped to bits and hauled into the belly of the ship. Crates, wooden ladles, and swab buckets added to the growing pile.

The boilermen burned the infrastructure as it was brought to them bit by bit. The ship worked up sufficient steam to get past Cape Flattery in one piece, then all was clear through the narrow Strait—on a day as blue and quiet as a dream of summer.

In Port Townsend at the top of the Sound, residents saw the long-lost steamer passing by. They came from their houses on the hilltop and hurried down into the town to line the shore, where they waved excitedly as the veritable ghost ship continued on its last legs toward Seattle. It was no ghost, but its presence was a miracle nonetheless. Even though it was unheard-of that a ship once lost should be returned by the sea, here was the impossible passing before their eyes.

Soon enough, all the newspapers up and down the coast were to feature articles about the miracle. Many a "hometown story" was made out of each passenger's perspective on their adventure. Twenty men and one woman were alive and in good health, and only poor Thomas the cook had been lost in the weird ordeal. Several home-coming celebrations were held in the wake of the near-disaster, while numerous hurrahs were shouted in the port taverns in praise of the pleasing outcome. The *Dora*'s name was bandied about not only from Seattle to Kodiak, but from Portland to San Francisco, from Honolulu to Macao, where she was acknowledged as the Miracle Ship motivated by her own private sentiment and resolve.

The *Dora* went into drydock in Seattle to undergo repairs. It was discovered that her hull had a great, gaping hole that should have been her death—and the death of all whom she carried. As improbability heaped upon improbability, the plain fact was that she had patched herself on the very reef that ripped her open. A rock from the Japanese reef had been imprisoned in her hull, and she had carried it all the way across the Pacific. For decades to follow, that rock lay on a dock in West Seattle as proof of the miraculous voyage of the steamship *Dora*.

She made her Alaska run for many years to follow, a sedate old lady who was finally satisfied with memories, having had her final fling. Today there is nothing of her left, for even the few charred planks that washed onto Richmond Beach have long since been devoured by worms.

The Door to Rainmaker's Lodge

A Legend of Stanley Park, Vancouver

THE PLACE WHERE Si'atmuulth and his family had their lodge was in present-day Stanley Park, near where the Lion's Gate Bridge now spans the uneasy waters of the inlet far below. The lodge was not of the large kind; there was room for one family only, which consisted of Si'atmuulth; his young wife, Neelah; his mother; some uncles; a few relatives of Neelah's, including her sister and her sister's husband; and several children, notably Si'atmuulth's toddler and newborn baby.

In the cedar lodge were two firepits on the packed earth floor, and above the firepits were smoke-windows with removable shutters. The door was low, square, and hinged with tough hide. Along two walls were benches with baskets and carved boxes underneath. On the walls hung painted mats with images of Big Beaver, Raven, and Black Fish. On a crossbeam was a carving of Thunderbird overlooking all. When Neelah first came to live with her older husband, there were none of these niceties.

Si'atmuulth's father and grandfather had lived long lives, but now they were dead. Si'atmuulth was himself long in the tooth, though he had a young wife. He had received from his father the secret of the rain. His father had received the same secret from his grandfather, and so on back in time. Thus Si'atmuulth was from an old family of

Rainmakers. When he opened the door of his lodge ever so slightly, a mist would cover the land. If he opened it a speck more, there would be a light drizzle. Still more, a good rain. If he threw the door open all the way, there would be a terrible storm until he drew it in and the storm subsided.

One day a council was arranged by Kapalana, chief of the Squamish. He sent invitations to the chiefs of other villages. They had very little in the way of important business to consider, if the truth be known, but they didn't let on that their main purpose was to smoke long pipes, gossip, and gamble with their peers. Rather, they gave the impression that grave issues were to be pondered and decided.

Si'atmuulth was invited to the council, but since he was not exactly a chief, not much was made of his arrival. Women gathered outside the Lodge of Chiefs to beat drums and sing about the power of the chiefs who brought peace and wealth to the people. They scarcely noticed that Si'atmuulth had walked by. They sang no praises to Si'atmuulth the Rainmaker.

Inside the lodge, Si'atmuulth was last to receive the pipe, as though he were an unimportant hanger-on who barely had the right to attend such a big meeting of visiting noblemen. Did they think themselves so mighty because they had royal blood and lived in enormous lodges? After much dawdling, and when pointless greetings were concluded, the council finally began. They spoke of such trivialities that the Rainmaker became convinced they were waiting for him to leave before they brought up anything important. In reality they were only waiting to be done with these matters so that they could play a game using black and white bones, and win each other's fine shirts. The true purpose of the meeting had somehow evaded Si'atmuulth's perception.

He'd had enough. He stood abruptly and marched out of the

lodge without farewells. The council chiefs assumed he was having a belly-ache and let him go. If they thought anything of his withdrawal, they thought only that it was too bad they would have no chance to win his shirt.

Si'atmuulth stamped home and threw the door open all the way. Immediately a storm burst from the sky. Lightning sparked against black clouds and water fell in torrents.

"Why are you bringing a storm?" asked his brother-in-law.

"What's it to you? I'm the Rainmaker! Show respect! How did I end up with such a family as this?"

"Do as you please," said his brother-in-law, and went to sit in a corner with his wife.

As he listened for sounds in the darkening dusk, Si'atmulth heard, between rolls of thunder, the song of village women, which had changed slightly. It was now about how the Chief of Gods was coming down on the rolling thunder to join his magic with the magic of the chiefs of the land.

The bad weather had not soured their spirits one bit! If he could get his door to open any farther, he'd bring such a deluge as to drown the lot of them! He let the storm continue for a week, until water ran into his own lodge and doused the firepits. His wife, Neelah, said, "Shut that door! This is too much, even for a cantankerous fool!"

"Call me what you please," said Si'atmuulth. "One way or another, I will have revenge for being slighted. The nobles and the villagers have taken me for granted. Chief Kapalana and the others will soon enough be reminded of my importance."

So saying, Rainmaker shut the door of his lodge, but not in obedience to his wife. With glue from a sturgeon's backbone, he sealed the door so tight that not the slightest draft could get through.

"What are you up to?" asked his elderly mother, her face a map of lines, her hair white as a mountaintop.

"You never mind," grumped her son. "It won't rain from now on. You and the uncles can dig a hole in that back corner and get what water our family requires. No one else will have any."

"It's not right," said his mother. "Your father would never have done this. Your grandfather, too."

"I am my own man! Why do the people fail to respect my art? Let them regret it!"

Neelah, holding her infant daughter while another child clung to her skirt, looked at her husband's handiwork. "How smart you think you are!" she said. "How will we come and go without a door?" She hated to be stern with Si'atmuulth, but of all the silly things he had ever done, and which she strove always to overlook, this outdid them all.

"I have put a ladder up to one of the smoke-windows," he said. "You can climb onto the roof and go down another ladder to get to the ground."

Before she said something she oughtn't, Neelah walked away in disgust.

At first no one knew something was amiss. Si'atmuulth's family became noticeably sullen, but the village itself was as yet unaffected. The days were long and sunny, and everyone was pleased with that. Children ran around rolling hoops and playing with toy spears. Young men played kick-ball along the banks of the Capilano River. Women wove hats and baskets, sitting on mats of braided cattail reeds outside the lodges. Si'atmuulth kept still about things, waiting impatiently for everyone to realize there would be no more rain ever again.

~~~~~

As the weeks passed, the vegetation withered, the ponds dried up, the creeks merely trickled. Si'atmuulth became increasingly unpleasant to his family. His in-laws packed their things and moved to the village where Neelah had come from. Some of his own blood relatives, beginning to feel hostility from the villagers, decided to move away to one of the islands. Neelah was herself tempted to leave, but it wasn't an easy decision, as she had two children.

Neelah said, "Mother and the children need more to drink than what is provided from that mud-hole you had us dig. Why don't you stop being so stubborn and unseal the door? Our family is breaking apart because of your actions. We are hated in the village. Swallow your pride, Si'atmuulth, my husband!"

Si'atmuulth heard but did not listen.

Chief Kapalana went up the dusty trail to the Rainmaker's lodge. The sweat ran down his back and soaked his robe. He was not a young man; he suffered from the heat. He knocked on the door with his walking-staff and the Rainmaker called from within, "Who's at my door?"

"It's your chief! Open the door at once!"

Si'atmuulth didn't like the tone of Chief Kapalana's voice. He climbed the ladder through the smoke-window and crawled on hands and knees to the edge of the roof. Chief Kapalana shaded his eyes and looked into the sun. He saw the Rainmaker's sharp shadow. He asked, "What have you been doing, Si'atmuulth? Why don't you open your door? Our children are dying of thirst."

"Ha ha! It took you all this time to figure it out? You thought so well of yourself and deprived me of honors. Now see who is greater! If I'm so useless, go find your own rain!"

Then Si'atmuulth crawled back through the smoke-window. He

The Door to Rainmaker's Lodge

scowled at Neelah, who sat in the corner with the two children, looking glum.

As the weeks progressed, the Capilano River ceased to flow, so there were no more fish. So too the game fled the region. The geese and swans bypassed the land of the Squamish. Snow vanished from all but the highest mountain ravines, and the great-horn goats wandered elsewhere. Children and old people died of weakness, hunger, and dehydration.

A council met on Howe Sound. All the nobles came, and not to gamble or gossip. All were serious of mien. Various plans were proposed, but nothing seemed feasible.

"If we give the Rainmaker many gifts and honors," said one nobleman, "maybe he will get over his snit."

"I have offered him many things," said Chief Kapalana. "I have placed the gifts before his lodge, but he never opens the door to claim them. He says we should have honored him before, now it is too late."

"Then let's break down his door!" said another. "Tear it right out of the wall!"

Chief Kapalana said, "If the door is broken, it may never rain again."

Another proposed, "We will elect someone to climb in his smokehole and kill him!"

Kapalana replied, "Only Si'atmuulth knows the secret of the raindoor. We dare not kill him."

Then the chief of the Insect Clan rose to speak. He was a small man whose tongue made a clicking sound, like a snap-beetle, when he talked. His tribe was called the Insect Clan because their totem spirit was the Ant. They possessed magic over fleas, lice, and mosquitoes. The Insect Chief presented his plan to the council. They agreed it was the best idea anyone had come up with.

That night, fleas invaded the Rainmaker's lodge. Si'atmuulth and his mother, wife, and toddler leapt out from their blankets and scratched themselves madly. Fleas hopped all around inside the hut. Then lice dropped from the painted mats hanging on the wall. They landed in the hair of Si'atmuulth and his family. The whole family scratched their heads and complained loudly.

They could not lay in their blankets. They could not sleep. The Rainmaker's wife made a fire, even though the night was hot, and filled the lodge with smoke, but the insects were not frightened away. Rather, the density of the insects tripled. Si'atmuulth's family coughed and choked on the smoke, scratched their bodies and heads, and stamped the floor, which was alive with lice and fleas.

Then the mosquitoes arrived in force. Everyone in the lodge was slapping their own flesh, beating themselves up, except the infant, who the insects miraculously avoided. The bigger child was not spared. He screamed and screamed. Si'atmuulth's old mother wept. Neelah was exasperated with everything and was on the verge of giving up and abandoning her husband. Raising her children alone in the woods would be better than this!

Just before dawn, the insects hopped and crept and flew away. The Rainmaker's family fell down, exhausted. They lay in a weary heap upon their bedding and were soon in a deep slumber.

That's when men of the Insect Clan lifted the shutter on the roof's smoke-window and peered into the interior of the Rainmaker's lodge. It was still smoky from Neelah's attempt to dispel the insects with smoke and fire.

The ladder was not at the smoke-window, so they lowered a rope into the lodge. A small, slender man slid down the rope like a spider. He crept silently about the lodge until he saw the Rainmaker's wife.

The Door to Rainmaker's Lodge

Swiftly and delicately he dislodged the baby from the woman's arms. Then he went back up the rope and the Insect Clansmen went into the hills to their hidden village.

Neelah was screaming and beating on the glued door. Si'atmuulth leapt up. They had slept past noon. He said, "Why are you hysterical?"

"They stole our baby! Our baby is gone!"

"How? The baby must be under a bench."

"She's not under a bench! I looked everywhere!"

"Then she crawled outside."

"How did she crawl outside? You glued the door shut!"

"That's right," said Si'atmuulth. He put a ladder to the smoke-window and climbed to the roof. He saw a council of nobles sitting down the slope on the dusty path sharing a pipe. Si'atmuulth called out, "Kapalana, you old coot! Bring my baby back here at once!"

"You let our children die of thirst," said Chief Kapalana, taking a long draw from the pipe before handing it to the Insect Chief.

"Return her! My wife will go crazy!"

"You were pitiless," said Chief Kapalana. "I must be pitiless as well."

"Where have you taken her?" Si'atmuulth demanded. "Bring her to me at once!"

"She is safe in the mountains," said Chief Kapalana. "Maybe you will never see her again."

Neelah heard this and screamed at Si'atmuulth, "Do what they say! Do what they say or I will kill you in your sleep!"

"What are your terms?" said Si'atmuulth.

"You will agree never to let the land dry out. You will never do a thing like this again. Your responsibility is great. You must always live up to your responsibility."

"Will I be respected in the council?"

"Respect is a thing to be earned and deserved, not bartered for."

"Will you at least bring back my baby?"

"Swear to uphold your responsibility, and she will be in your lodge before the first rain stops."

Si'atmuulth climbed back inside his lodge. He took a knife and cut the glue out of the seams of the door. Then he opened the door a short distance. The sky began to cloud and a mist drifted in from Howe Sound. He pushed the door farther, and a drizzle fell from heaven. He opened it halfway, and a good hard rain began at once to revive the parched land. That same afternoon, Neelah received her infant from a princess of the Insect People. The baby was laughing, and in her pudgy hands she held a tiny cage with a cricket inside.

Si'atmuulth never again misbehaved. To this day, when native peoples of Vancouver hear the rain at their doors, they say, "Si'atmuulth is keeping his word!"

Notes, Sources, and Commentaries

THE RUINED IDYLL

F. H. Sayer gave the present legend the dubious title "Why the Indian Fears Golden Hair" in the May 1899 issue of his likable journal *Oregon Native Son*. The Multnomah Falls myth came to him via an old man, unnamed by Sayer, who was generally reticent about sharing his tribe's tales. The quiet native usually passed by the immigrants' houses without incident. But one day he spotted a recent arrival coming out of a cabin. At the sight of her pale hair, he was taken aback. Rallying to the occasion of having encountered a supernatural creature, he began to circle her with "as rapid and active a dance as his aged limbs could perform, accompanied by a low and weird chant." Afterward, realizing his error, he volunteered, by way of excusing his behavior, the legend of Multnomah Falls.

Fred Sayer noted that Northwest native peoples rarely saw blonde hair even after the arrival of whites. This was, after all, in days before just anyone could become a blonde with the assistance of chemistry. The reason the Multnomah Falls Goddess had white hair (not blonde) was that in winter Wahseakli reappeared in the falls' towering shapes of snowy white ice. Native white-haired "sorceresses" are remembrances of a universal type of Earth mother who is simultaneously maiden and hag, as in the case of the Modoc Earth Maiden Latkakawas, who was eternally young when seen from a distance but a hag when seen up close. We have intimations of the old-young Earth mother in the well-known "Bridge of the Gods" myth, wherein the Goddess Loowit (Mount St. Helens) appears by turns as a hag and a maiden and is courted (like Wahseakli) by two suitors.

Pioneers seem to have known something of the Multnomah Falls Goddess. A poem by J. W. Whalley called "Multnomah Falls," in *The Pacific*

Monthly for April 1900, celebrates the falls as a Bride, the Columbia her Groom, and Nature a priestess performing the wedding ceremony. Elva J. Smith gave another legend, again in verse, as "Multnomah," in *Oregon Teachers Monthly* (February 1904). Here the heroine's family is slain by a cruel suitor who takes her captive. As last of her tribe, she refuses to submit to the suitor, but throws herself into the Willamette River, where she is transformed into a water rose. Harry Lauren Wells's annotated poem *Multnomah, a Legend of the Columbia* (1923; originally in *Pacific Magazine*, January 1897) tells the story of the Multnomah Goddess as sacrificial virgin, with comparisons to Greco-Roman divinities. Susan Williamson Smith christianizes the sacrifical-virgin story in her long poem *The Legend of Multnomah Falls* (1905), complete with references to Jesus. This pioneer coöptation of the aboriginal myth depicts a pure maiden who agrees to be sacrificed to stop a plague. She leaps to her doom from atop the falls in order that her lover and her village will recover from the illness. The pioneer fantasy that one young woman's suicide saved these people is baffling, given that the Multnomahs never recovered from epidemics that peaked in 1832.

I have avoided the pioneer version in composing "The Ruined Idyll." The interested reader may wish to refer to Ella E. Clark's "A Legend of Multnomah Falls" in *Indian Legends of the Pacific Northwest* (1953) for a retelling of the story as told by white immigrants.

THE LEGEND OF CHIEF PATKANIM'S SPIES

Sam MacDougall came to young Snohomish City in 1888. Toward the end of his life, in the early 1960s, he told this historical tale to reporter Chuck Rice. I stumbled upon Rice's article "Legend of the Foe Above Snoqualmie Falls," dated April 26, 1962, in a clipping file in the University of Washington Special Collections Library. Information regarding Chief Patkanim's role in the wars between Western and Eastern Washington tribes near and around Snoqualmie Pass can be found on page 60 of Clarence B. Bagley's *History of Snohomish County* (1926), and an overview of this great chief's career is available in Edmond S. Meany's "Chief Patkanim" in the *Washington Historical Quarterly* (July 1924), written on the occasion of the dedication of an impressive monument on his grave in Tulalip. He died in 1858. Though his age was not known, he was probably middle-aged and should have lived many more vigorous years. The cause of his premature death is unrecorded.

Many old documents praise Patkanim for his later support of whites but fault his earlier "savagery." Other documents reveal a fear and dislike for Chief Patkanim even as he supported peace with the whites. Some of this attitude survives down to our day. A recent diatribe against "the red man Patkanim" in an unfortunate essay, "Cheating Chief Unscrupulous," can be found in Marge Davenport's *Fabulous Folks of the Old Northwest* (1986). The essay, riddled with adjectives like "unsavory" and "despicable," deprecates his delivery of enemy heads to whites in exchange for his captain's pay. A more reasonable judgment can be found in "Sealth and the Allied Tribes" in J. A. Costello's *The Siwash: Their Life Legends and Tales* (1895), which quotes Samuel Coombs's report: "A son of Pat Kanim told me his father had been a good, true friend of the whites during the Indian war, and he corroborated what A. A. Denny has said in his history of the war. He said that Mr. Denny had with good reason placed confidence in his father, notwithstanding that others thought he was not worthy of it." No one has as yet written an honest, balanced overview of Chief Patkanim's activities, with as much admiration for his early successes against whites as for his attempts to forge bonds with whites to preserve the Snoqualmie, Snohomish, and smaller allied tribes.

The Snoqualmie Falls legend could well be true in its entirety. First of all, the episode plays off the actual political situation among the tribes on the two sides of the Cascades prior to white settlement near Snoqualmie Pass. The attitude of the Sahaptan-speaking, horse-riding Yakamas against the Salish-speaking canoe tribes may be gauged by the popularity among the Yakamas of a myth about Speelyi (Coyote) and Wishpoosh (Evil Big Beaver), who warred against one another in Lake Keechelas near the pass, with Wishpoosh getting the worst of it. This myth essentially demonizes lake- and river-focused "beaver" lifestyles in favor of the Yakamas' (and Coyote's) drier habitat.

Some might argue that the Snoqualmie Trail (which follows the Snoqualmie, Snohomish, and Cedar rivers and tributaries all the way to Puget Sound) was too well known by the surrounding peoples for the present legend to function as history. Yakamas as much as any other Northwest tribe relied on this trail, for Snoqualmie Pass was the most reliable of the handful of seasonal routes through the Cascades. Indeed, the Kittitas Valley was the location of an enormous annual festival that long predated the appearance of whites. This festival brought thousands of Native Americans together from Idaho, Oregon, British Columbia, and all over Washington, to trade coastal shells for inland buffalo rugs and to socialize, gamble, engage in sports, gossip, and mediate disputes. Furthermore, since Kittitas Indians lived with Snoqualmies at the Tokul Creek village below the falls, they would certainly be cognizant of the danger the falls presented. All this argues against the historicity of Yakama warriors not knowing what they were headed for.

Yet the more distant plateau Yakamas were not as apt to have a realistic sense of the dangers of the mountains. If the legend of the spies is true, then old Sam MacDougall must have had it from a Salish friend who remembered those days. There is independent confirmation in a Twana story in which the Snoqualmies provide a group of Yakamas with a canoe so they can go to Puget Sound to collect shellfish (a likely excuse!). Although the Snoqualmies warn the Yakamas about the falls, the latter leave their horses behind, jump in the canoe, and tumble over the falls. This story can be found in William W. Elmendorf's *Twana Narratives: Native Historical Accounts of a Coast Salish Culture* (1993) under the droll heading "Yakimas Are Not Smart West of the Mountains."

THE PHANTOM SHIP

John Hahn mentioned Pier 70's phantom ship in his article "Pier 70 Haunted by Rumors of a Ghost" in the *Seattle Post-Intelligencer* (May 2, 1989). Better-known than the ship, however, is the pier's ghost, whose identity is a mystery. Brad Aylward, a manager of Pier One Imports, said, "I'd discount it except that reports of a ghost have come from a lot of different people, very reputable people . . . including my wife." Amy Aylward had several uncanny experiences. Cash registers would suddenly open after hours while she was alone, though cash was never taken. Brad admitted there were times, after closing, when he became convinced someone was still in the store, but upon searching found no one. Norman Foster ran a shop near the end of the pier, where he felt that the ghost tried to communicate with him. He saw it as "a pillar of smoke swirling above a chair as though something or someone was trying to manifest."

The history of Pier 70 goes back to 1889, when the partnership of Ainsworth and Dunn built a 550-foot pier and warehouse across from what is now the Spaghetti Factory. Originally designated Pier 14, it was the stopping point of Britain's Blue Funnel Line and Germany's Hamburg American Line. The Coast Guard changed the pier's number when more piers were added at the south end of the waterfront.

Edward Dunn, a descendant of the pier's original owner, noted, "In the old days, lots of people were done in and tossed into the Sound." The pier ghost could be one such victim. Though usually described as an invisible presence, those who have seen him materialize state that he is a bearded sailor in a dark green peacoat, known affectionately as Patrick. John Latharakis, whose Tabula Rasa Press sold miniature books on the pier, recently informed me that the ghost remains well known and has acquired some new traits: he is currently believed to be a peg-legged sea captain who scurries about so swiftly it is hard to catch more than a passing glimpse of him.

THE SPIRIT ELK

There used to be a Wasco footpath running from The Dalles to the Sandy River, which passed Lost Lake, the most beautiful and remote of the lakes associated with Mount Hood. This triangular lake, in Hood River County in northwestern Oregon, was an elk feeding ground; hence the Wascos hunted there. "The Elk Hunter," in Franz Boas's *Chinook Texts* (1894), tells of a hunter who caught a beautiful woman in an elk trap, showed her to villagers, in consequence of which the hunter and villagers died. Years later a young orphan caught her, and she advised him over the years, as he matured. From him other hunters obtained powers of the hunt. A version of this legend was heard by Ella P. Robert on a camping trip. She retold it in the December 1920 issue of the mountaineers' journal *Mazama* under the title "Lost Lake." This is the version that speaks of a false seer's jealousy and upon which Ella E. Clark seems to have based her retelling, "The Elk Spirit of Lost Lake," in *Indian Legends of the Pacific Northwest* (1953).

Another variant is "The White Elk of Lost Lake" in *Mount Hood* (1940), a book compiled by participants in the writers' program of the Work Projects Administration. This time, the hunter's foe is a second hunter, jealous of his rival's status as champion. It is the foe rather than the champion who slays elk in excess. By this feat, he comes to be regarded as the finer of the two hunters. The protagonist becomes angry with his spirit guardian for allowing his championship to be exceeded, and in his anger puts an arrow into the heart of the white elk, who leaps into Lost Lake. The champion, regretting his temper, leaps into the lake to see if he can rescue the injured elk. The rival hunter leaps in as well, hoping to acquire the guardian spirit as his own. All three are drawn to the bottom and never seen again. Two loons heard for years afterward were regarded as the ghosts of the rival hunters.

The best version is "The Hunter Who Had an Elk for a Guardian Spirit," collected by Jeremiah Curtin in the 1880s and edited by Edward Sapir in *Wasco Tales and Myths* (1909). Here the hunter lives on Dog River, the name the Wascos gave to Hood River, a southern tributary of the Columbia. Curtin's Wasco text has neither the false shaman nor the rival hunter, but, rather, a difficult father. By way of prologue to the main tale, we learn that the father had a scar on his forehead obtained in his childhood in an encounter with an elk doe. He had tried to kill her fawn and was attacked by the protective mother. In later years he remained proud of his hard-earned scar and was spiteful toward his son, who was an excellent archer but only killed small game.

This Wasco version is acutely anti-romantic. The son simply lacks the capacity to do great things. It is the guardian doe who inspires the slaughter in order to prove to the father how much power the young man possesses. Immediately afterward, she turns against her ward, delivering him to the God-elk, as much in malice against the father as against the son. The message here seems to be that power given to the weak will destroy the bearer, unlike the versions that suppose a false seer inducing unnecessary turmoil. The Wasco story has a subtext suggesting the father is not wrong to deal harshly with his impuissant son.

Notes, Sources, and Commentaries

In 1926, Joe Hunt, a Klickitat from the same general region as the Wascos, told his version, "The Hunter Obtains a Deer Hunting Power," preserved in Jacob Melville's *Northwest Sahaptin Texts, Part I* (1934). This tale is entirely unsympathetic to the father, who tells his son he lost his leg to an elk. The elk reveals to the son that his father lied about his youthful prowess, for in actuality he lost his leg when a log rolled on him. The son goes to live in the lake as preferable to staying with a lying father.

It's conceivable the versions retold by Clark and Robert are influenced by Gustav Flaubert's classic novelette "The Legend of St. Julian the Hospitaler," which he founded on a vignette from the medieval European anthology *Gesta Romanorum ("Tales of the Monks")*. Julian was similarly punished for excessive slaughter on the hunt. In death he, too, was reunited with his guardian (Christ) who had previously appeared to the grief-stricken hospitaler as a sick old man.

GHOUL JOHN AND THE CORPSE

The Chinook ideal of beauty was a straight line from tip of nose to top of head. Commonly worn conical hats, woven of cedar bark and root, increased the peaked appearance of the wearers' heads. Nearly all of the Columbia River tribes were flatheads—a look achieved in the cradle, when the head was strapped in such a way as to reshape it according to the fashion. This also broadened the face, so that flatheads had large-seeming, bright eyes. Only slaves lacked the flathead appearance. As the practice died, it became increasingly restricted to women, but initially it had no relationship to gender.

Whites were both repulsed and fascinated by the practice. There were many infant deaths due to smallpox and a malarialike fever; it was the flathead skulls of these dead children that were most prized among whites, who considered them charmingly macabre decorations. This white predilection for rummaging amidst the dead was incredible to Chinook peoples, for whom grave robbing was both novel and incomprehensible. Given how blithely immigrant whites robbed native peoples, whether living or dead, it is ironic that many explorers and early settlers complained that Indians were such thieves that anything easily carted off would disappear.

The character of Ghoul John is based on naturalist John Townsend, who came to the Columbia River on the ship of Captain Nathaniel Wyeth. Wyeth's Fort William was on Wapato Island, shortly afterward known as Sauvies Island, after the dairyman of the Hudson's Bay Company, who took over Wyeth's headquarters. Sauvies Island, about fifteen miles long and four and a half miles at its greatest width, lies about twelve miles northwest of Portland's business center, at the mouth of the Willamette River where it converges with the Columbia. When Lewis and Clark visited the region, there were seven villages on the island, mostly belonging to the Multnomahs, with populations ranging from under two hundred to over a thousand. But four years before the arrival of Townsend, a malaria-like epidemic introduced by white trade ships at Fort Vancouver eradicated this native people, who never again sustained a viable population on the former Wapato Island. A historical overview can be found in Roy F. Jones's privately printed *Wappato Indians: Their History and Prehistory* (1972).

Above and beyond the usual white disregard for the sacredness of native burial grounds, Townsend possessed the irresponsible curiosity of an amoral scientist. He was adept at justifying himself even while stating explicitly his awareness that his activities were a sacrilege. With the exception of Lean Elk's supernatural experience—drawn from a native belief that the soul was a miniature replica of the living person—the entirety of this story is true; all the activities of Ghoul John have been drawn without exaggeration from Townsend's personal account in his *Narrative of a Journey Across the Rocky Mountains to the Columbia River* (1839).

THE WOMAN WHO TURNED TO SOAP

The main facts of this remarkable incident are told by Ellia E. Conklin in "The Lady of the Lake: Tale of the Corpse Turned to Soap Keeps Lake Crescent Bubbling with Intrigue" in the *Seattle Post-Intelligencer* (October 30, 1990). Conklin drew in part from a florid account written in 1942 by "a bulldog detective," Hollis B. Fultz, for *True Detective* as "The Corpse that Came Back." The story is repeated as "Clever D. A. Solves Mystery" in Marge Davenport's *Fabulous Folks of the Old Northwest* (1986). I have adapted the actualities of the murder mystery to fashion an adventure for Penelope Pettiweather, a character already familiar to those of you who've read my previous volume, *The Mysterious Doom and Other Ghostly Tales of the Pacific Northwest* (1992).

Lake Crescent is on the northern Olympic Peninsula fourteen miles west of Port Angeles, at the northern foot of the Olympic Mountains. At more than eight miles long, it is the third-largest lake in Western Washington; its shorelines are precipitous. There are much older legends about the lake than the one I selected. One of the key myths is given in Albert Reagan and L. V. W. Walters's "Tales from the Hoh and Quileute" in the *Journal of American Folk-Lore* (October–December 1933). The Klallam and Quileute peoples met in battle, shedding much blood. Mount Storm King grew annoyed by the noise and slaughter. He broke off a piece of rock from his crown and hurled it into the valley, killing both armies. The rock dammed a stream, creating Lake Crescent.

Yet another origin myth is given under the heading "Some Legends of the Olympics" in *The Washington Business Woman* (June 1934), probably by editor Lulu M. Fairbanks. A deity whom the article identified as a female angel covered the area with a glacier because she was angry with the animals living there. Later she repented and scooped out a hollow, where vegetation then reappeared. Years afterward the Klallams discovered a lake in that place. This so-called "angel" was evidently God-woman or Earth Mother, who in another myth lived near Lake Quinault but visited other places in the world rendering judgments, punishing and rewarding. It is probable that Mount Storm King, overlooking Lake Crescent, was regarded as female prior to the coming of the whites (just as Mount Rainier and Mount St. Helens were the goddesses Tahoma and Loowit, respectively). Mary Gay Morse, in *Lore of Olympic-Land* (1924), tells a "Sleeping Beauty" legend of the Olympic Mountains Goddess, who from her bed of snow and rock controls the winds and guides the destiny of the city of Port Angeles even to the present day.

THE GIRL WHO LOVED THE FOREST

Lake Nahketa, today called Lake Sutherland after the first white man to see it, lies twelve miles west of Port Angeles, not far from Crescent Lake, in Clallam County. The first written form of the story was that of Mary Gay Morse in a quaint volume of tales, *Lore of Olympia-Land* (1924), also issued under the title *Wayside Sketches*. Two later versions draw exclusively from Morse's tale, for she seems to be the only authority for this legend. The region Morse wrote about was ruled by the Klallams, although she says only that her sources were friends among "the Siwash." Siwash does not indicate a tribe, but is an antiquated term for coastal peoples, a corruption of the French word for "savage," and rather derogatory even if not consciously intended as such. In all likelihood Morse heard the story from an old Klallam woman, for she noted that only the Indian grandmothers remembered Nahketa.

Why the Loon Cries

Mason Lake is about four miles long but narrow in width. It lies north of Shelton on the Olympic Peninsula, eight miles southwest of Belfair. It has long been believed that Mason Lake is haunted. The sound of the loon represents the sad calling of ghosts and lake-spirits in many legends throughout the Northwest. The story of the Swoquad ("Loon") was told by Nisqually mothers to their children as a warning about the lake, and in a more general sense to encourage obedience. The legend was reported by James Wickersham in "Nusqually Mythology: Studies of the Washington Indians" in the October 1898 issue of California's *The Overland Monthly*. A shorter version, which assumes the mother had several children who turned into loons, occurs as "Origin of the Loons" in Volume 2 of Edward Evans's *History of the Pacific Northwest* (1889). This latter version had a different moral, warning mothers not to be overly strict.

Place of Thunder

This tale is retold from a legend reported by Donald Hines in his excellent volume *Ghost Voices: Yakima Indian Myths, Legends, Humor, and Hunting Stories* (1992). It was originally collected in 1915 from a Yakama-Klickitat hunter. Enum-klah-pah, now called Snow Lake, is on the border of Kittitas and King counties, three miles northwest of Snoqualmie Pass. It is three-fourths of a mile wide and two miles long, small but exceedingly deep. It has no visible source or outlet, hence no fish lived in it naturally. A lack of fish was invariably cause for concluding a lake was evil. It was believed such lakes had a dreadful influence upon the surrounding vicinity. The Yakamas believed Snow Lake was the domain of the Qui-yiahs, five giant brothers who killed hunters. Willful, disobedient children used to be taken up to Enum-klah-pah and tied to a tree near the lake and left overnight as punishment, having been carefully instructed that if they untied themselves, they would die. This type of punishment probably originated as part of initiatory rites at puberty, for acquiring a protective spirit, when entering a secret society, or other similar occasions.

Not all legends of Snow Lake are frightful. One whimsical belief is that the *q'whe-hinch,* large pearl clams, roll out of Snow Lake to bask in sunlight. If anyone tries to pick one up, it rolls back into the safety of the lake. Yet the lake's key legends regard white dogs, white elk, white otters, and other ghostly animals seen swimming therein.

THE VANISHED GREAT LAKE

This story exists in many sketchy forms well known among peoples of Eastern Washington. Geologists have proven the reality of such a lake, while archaeologists have established the length of time the region was inhabited by the ancestors of today's Native Americans. The scientific evidence is in accord with the legend. We may well regard the tale as a recollection, preserved in oral tradition, of the era following the Ice Age. As traditionally told, it regarded the existence and destruction of the lake, followed by the establishment of the settlement below Spokane Falls, though without inclusion of specific heroic figures such as I have imagined to be Chief Whistelpossum's ancestors. I think his spirit will not mind my invention.

The outline of the story was received by Major R. D. Gwydir when he was the United States Indian agent of the Colville reservation. It was told to him by Chief Whistelpossum, also called Chief Lot, in his old age. Major Gwydir characterized Whistelpossum as one of the most honest men he'd ever met. The narrative remained in Gwydir's handwritten manuscript of a lecture, which languished for many years in the Spokane

Public Library. An editor for *The Washington Historical Quarterly* copied it out by hand for the April 1907 issue, where it appeared under the title "Prehistoric Spokane—An Indian Legend." Several later versions appear in sundry books without noticeable differences.

There is a Coyote myth about Spokane Falls worth noting. When humanity was yet new, the animals who had previously ruled the world lingered. Coyote saw a young maiden living in a prosperous village high up the river. He asked the chief to give her in marriage. The chief, alarmed at the idea of his daughter wedding an animal, refused. Coyote, outraged, raised Spokane Falls to keep the salmon from reaching the village. According to "How Spokane Falls Were Made"—from "Folk-lore of the Flathead Indians" in *The Journal of American Folk-Lore* (October–December 1901)—Coyote's vengeance was against the Pend Oreille tribe, who dwelt, among other places, far above the falls. Chief Whistel-possum had a different version of this myth, told by the people below the falls. Coyote menaced sundry peoples until they joined together to catch him in a snare. They cut his carcass into many pieces so that all the tribes could eat him, after which they prospered. A fascinating commentary on what may have brought the animal age to an end: human predation!

BONE-CLEANER OF BLUE LAKE

The dry beds of the Moses Coulee and Grand Coulee were formed in prehistoric times when the Columbia River changed its course. Virginia Beck's essay "Grand Coulee: A Home of Strange Spirits" in *Pacific Wilderness Journal* (February–March 1975), noted that Sanpoils and Nespelems responded to the weirdness of the Coulee's gigantic deep canyons, dry streambeds, and isolated lakes by assuming it was a place of evil powers. Alexander Ross, a clerk of the Astor Fur Company, described the Coulee in 1810 as being feared by the Sanpoils as the home of many strange spirits. The Coulee was supposedly dug by Coyote—a myth that finds an echo in the Paul Bunyan tale of Babe the Blue Ox having drunk the Coulee dry.

That part of the Coulee known as the Moses Coulee is northeast of Wenatchee, Washington. It was here Chief Moses and his band dwelt for fifty years prior to his death in 1903. The band was afterward relocated to the Colville reservation near Okanogan. A brief history is given by J. C. Scott in "Indian Lore and Moses Coulee" in the July 1928 *Puget Sound Electrical Journal*.

The key events of the bone-cleaner legend were told by Bob Covington, a half-Sanpoil of the Colville reservation, who died in 1930. Covington told the story in the autumn of 1923 to Verne F. Ray, who included it as tale number 35 of "Sanpoil Folk Tales" in *The Journal of American Folk-Lore* (April–June 1933). Mr. Covington told other Coulee lake and river legends as well. A spirit-woman who appeared on the surface of Lake Omak west of Sanpoil territory usually tried to drown passers-by. A narrow stretch of trail between the cliffs and the Sanpoil River is haunted by a ghost that chases people. At Buffalo Lake in the middle of Sanpoil territory, a spirit "as big as a house loomed up out of the lake," appearing to travellers as an evil omen.

In retelling the story of the bone-cleaner, I added the character of Ralph. I've also incorporated a couple additional bits of Blue Lake/Grand Coulee lore found under the heading "Grand Coulee" in Richard Steele and Arthur Rose's *An Illustrated History of the Big Bend Country* (1904).

Historically the Sanpoils have been an independent-minded people who embraced the Dreamer faith and guarded the traditional ways, rejecting government "assistance" and missionaries alike. They refused to use modern implements, preferring traditional tools and weapons.

Their original nation was at the confluence of the Sanpoil River and the Columbia.

YOUNG MAN WHO BECAME WEARY

The exact location of the village in this story is today the Bush Pacific Pioneer State Park near Bay Center on Willapa Bay (formerly Shoalwater Bay), in southwestern Washington. Today the native peoples of the Willapa Bay region live mainly on the Shoalwater reservation at the north point of the bay. Shoalwater Bay Tribe has a mixed Chinook and Chehalis ancestry, but the present tale was of Upper Chinook origin, although it may have been inherited from an Athabascan people called the Kwalhioquas, who died out from plagues of the 1850s. Isaac H. Whealdon in "Stories and Sketches from Pacific County" (*Washington Historical Quarterly,* July 1913) offers an "origin" story of how Willapa Bay became inhabited when the tribe arrived in a giant canoe from a lost homeland. This would fit well with the Kwalhioquas, who were the only Athabascan speakers of the region and so seemed truly transplanted from elsewhere, but it equally suits the Chinook-Chehalis people who moved suddenly into the region as the Kwalhioquas died out. "Young Man Who Became Weary" is in any case unique to Willapa Bay, with no very close parallel in the lore of other tribes.

The present retelling adheres fairly closely to the story as collected by Franz Boas in 1891, included under the untranslatable title "Emogoalekc" in *Kathlamet Texts* (1901). The Upper Chinooks spoke Kathlamet, the original language of this tale. Kathlamet was spoken from Astoria, Oregon, northward to the southern edge of Grays Harbor, Washington, embracing the whole of Willapa Bay, which lies between these two points; and it was a dominant language inland all the way to Mount Rainier. Yet when Boas received the stories in his collection from

Charles Cultee of Bay Center, Washington, Cultee was one of only three persons living who spoke the Kathlamet dialect, and he was the only one of those three who could recite Kathlamet traditions.

I was intrigued by the "weepiness" of the tale, which is greatly heightened compared to most such stories, and by the nearly homosexual closeness of the emotional youths. Intersexual characteristics and homosexual behavior were not uncommon among tribal peoples. There are other examples of homosexuality and/or gender dysphoria in tales of tribal leaders, though in later decades such individuals were more apt to become shamans rather than chiefs, and later still, after the influence of Christian missionaries, they were increasingly apt to become outcast. The present tale presents this aspect of native lifestyles circumspectly, steeped in the "innocence" of the sorts of youthful crushes boys have for boys. Yet this *is* the very element that proves individual uniqueness and serves to foreshadow a commoner's future status as chief. It would seem, as well, to underscore the pro-underdog sentiments of the legend generally, evidenced by the tale's acceptance of a marriage between a princess and a commoner, and the sympathy expressed for the love felt by a prince for a slave girl.

THE SWAN QUEEN AND THE ELK CHILD

Horsethief Lake on the Washington side of the Columbia River is not necessarily the location of this myth. The original location may have been a shallow lake in the Klickitat Valley, or a minor lake near Mount Adams. That lake subsequently dried up, causing the swan-goddess to move to a new residence. Horsethief Lake is the likeliest candidate, so I've made that lake the scene of all the action.

G. B. Kuykendall's long chapter "The Indians of the Pacific Northwest: Their Legends, Myths, Religion and Customs," in Volume 2 of

Elwood Evans's *History of the Pacific Northwest: Oregon and Washington* (1889), tells of the swan-goddess and the elk-child, under the heading "Mountain Lake Myths." Kuykendall identified the tale as involving a Wishram maiden, though he heard it from a Klickitat on the Yakama reservation. It is possible the maiden was called a Wishram because the Klickitat storytellers preferred to blame their neighbors at The Dalles, and not themselves, for the destructive selfishness the maiden represented.

Melville Jacobs includes another version of the Klickitat elk-child legend as "The Girl Carried Off and Made Pregnant by Elk," in *Northwest Sahaptin Texts I* (1934). Jacobs collected the tale in 1926, as told by Joe Hunt, a Klickitat. Whereas Kuykendall supposes the maiden urinated where the elk had previously urinated, the tale as collected by Jacobs assumes the reverse. Both take for granted that this activity could induce pregnancy. We may well guess women were careful in those days where they peed!

In Kuykendall's version, the elk-child was killed outright by the heartless mother so that it would remain unknown that she had birthed him. But the 1926 version shows a mother who feels sorrow when the boy turns into an elk and escapes. The purpose of both was to explain why elk no longer came to lakes of the area, though once they were plentiful in Klickitat country and around Horsethief Lake. The legend resembles the Lost Lake legend of the nearby Wascos (told as "The Spirit Elk" elsewhere in this collection), in that both stories are about individuals who are not morally strong enough to cope constructively with the spirit-power they obtain.

The Changelings

Dr. Albert S. Gatschet received this Wapato Lake legend from a Tualatin woman named Emmy, and recorded it in 1877 in Emmy's own language, Kalapuyan. Emmy was the wife of Qa'yaqats. Her family had been wealthy and had dwelt at Gaston Lake southwest of Hillsborough. But everything was taken from them, and they ended up on the Grand Ronde reservation. Tualatin country in northwestern Oregon was in the upper Willamette Valley above the region of the Yamhills. The lake where the present tale is set is in the Coast Range foothills southwest of Forest Grove. Because it overflooded annually, and because native women waded in the flooded areas to dig camas roots in spring, it was sometimes called Step In The Water Lake.

Emmy's story was printed alongside its translation, "The Water Being," in Melville Jacobs's *Kalapuya Texts* (1945), together with variations by Tualatins named Dave Y'to'gawa and Enimdi. Dr. Gatschet had earlier published a version as "Amhuluk, the Monster of the Mountain Pool" in his article "Oregonian Folklore" in the *Journal of American Folklore* (January–March 1891). I have consulted all versions. Emmy thought only the horn of the Huluk (or Amhuluk) had spots, but Enimdi said the whole body of the water being was spotted, adding the detail that the being had a spotted dog as a pet. Also, in Enimdi's version, the older boy who escaped the Huluk died the next day, though Emmy did not note this detail; the story may once have been even more despairing.

The meaning of the Huluk tradition had been nearly forgotten and was somewhat incomplete even in the 1870s. By World War I, the Kalapuya language was no longer spoken. The Tualatins who were asked about the Huluk were by then under the general impression that it must have been a type of whale, despite descriptions of it having four legs and perhaps a porcupine's rump. They had evidently combined the Huluk tale with lake-whale legends, but lake whales, unlike the Huluk, were not considered evil. Typically, lake-whale stories involved underground rivers connecting lakes to the sea, or landlocked whales created famous rivers by plowing their way to the sea. Taking off from Emmy's uncertain allusion to the water being's porcupine rump, I've imagined something part porcupine and part beaver, as I find the story more closely related to monster-beaver legends than to lake-whale legends.

In Roberta L. Hall's *The Coquille Indians: Today, Yesterday and Tomorrow* (1984) from a Lake Oswego publisher, there is described a Coos Bay monster that got a canoe stuck on its single horn and was burned to death when it became wedged between trees. Some Coquilles said it was a rhinocerous that escaped from a passing ship, but chances are this is a revised remembrance of the older Huluk legend. If we dare to believe an oral tradition could preserve some faint recollection of beasts extinct in North America for 40,000 years, we might suppose the Huluk was an actual water rhino such as once dwelt in the Northwest. At the very least, one-horned fossils of the extinct giant may have been discovered from time to time, inspiring legends—much as discovery of pterodactyl fossils inspired Northwest myths of monster mosquitoes. George F. Beck's article "Blue Lake Rhino" in the *Spokesman Review* (December 30, 1951) tells of a rhino fossil found in the upper Coulee. Complete rhino skeletons have also been found in Nebraska.

The Wapato legend is on the one hand a nursery tale with a bogey meant to warn children away from a lake wherein they might drown. But on a far more tragic level, it is a tale of parental grief over the actual loss of children to disease. A very long time ago the tale may have regarded drowned children, and there would have been no reference to a spotted horn, nor would the escaping boy have become spotted. But the detail of spotting shows this legend to express the horror of smallpox epidemics which Europeans spread throughout South and North America. Pox and malaria forshadowed the coming of the whites as a fearful "advance guard," for, by the time Lewis and Clark appeared in Oregon, half the native population of the Columbia River had already died of illness brought by cross-cultural fur trading. In many places only one in ten members of any given tribe survived, and these few survivors merged into mixed tribes, which caused their unique cultures to be jumbled together or lost. What had once been the most populous region anywhere in Native America became a series of ghostly, abandoned villages. This means, of course, that even the great linguists and ethnographers of the late nineteenth century—who have preserved for us a surprising store of knowledge regarding Northwest native languages, ways, and beliefs—were detailing cultures the richness of which was already degraded and in many cases recalled by none but the oldest tribal members.

Very likely the tradition of the spotted Huluk faded when pox became less relentless and less deadly. Hence the nature and character of the Huluk was forgotten. Even so, some slight memory of the water being did survive into the twentieth century, for there was a Huluk footprint celebrated at Gaston, Oregon, at least until mid-century, and a few old-timers may yet know where that footprint can be found.

WHEN THE WOMAN CHIEF WAS YOUNG

At the summit of the Cascade Range near Jacksonville in southern Oregon is an almost perfectly round lake, with a shocking depth of 1,996 feet. The Klamaths called it Lake Giwas or Gaywas. The first white man to see it was John W. Hillman, who stumbled on it by accident on June 12, 1853. It was initially christened with a variety of names, including Deep Blue Lake, Mysterious Lake, or Lake Majesty, although others called it The Hole in the Ground. On August 4, 1869, a party from Jacksonville (evidently including Hillman) selected the name Crater Lake, since it is indeed the crater of a prehistoric volcano, the top of which has vanished. The mountain itself was christened Mazama by Fay Fuller von Briesen on behalf of the Mazamas mountain climbing society on August 21, 1896, though it had been known to the Klamaths as Llao Yaina, "Llao's Mountain." The eroded peak was once twice as high as Mount Hood! On the western side of the lake is a cinder cone reaching 845 feet above the water; this is Wizard Island, atop which is an extinct crater, a fabulous volcano within a volcano. Toward the eastern shore is a jagged rock island called the Phantom Ship (the "spirit-canoe" of the myth), which resembles a tall ship with trees for masts. No other isles mar the mirrorlike, azure surface.

A Klamath legend explaining the crater's origin was retold by Charles Erskine Scott Wood as "How the Spirit of Coyote Passed from Earth" in *A Book of Tales* (1891; 1929). Coyote fell in love with a star-maiden. She took him up and up into the sky. When he complained of the height, she dropped him. Where he landed a crater was formed, and Coyote's blood turned to water.

William Gladstone Steel, as he outlines in *The Mountains of Oregon* (1890), was instrumental in having the Crater Lake area declared a national park. In 1885, a day after Chief Allen David of the Klamaths told him of the demon of the lake, Steel officially preserved the name of Llao Rock, wherein the spirit demon resides. Llao Rock, at the western lakeshore, rises 2,000 feet above the water. Chief David's "Legend of the Llaos," as given in *Steel Points* (January 1902), regarded a young Klamath who climbed Llao Rock several times over a period of months, envisioned wonderful beings in the lake, and after ascetic practices obtained a spirit power. This youth later slew one of Llao's monsters, in consequence of which Llao's demonic warriors captured him, took him to the top of the rock, cut his throat, dismembered him, and threw his parts into the lake to be eaten by the crawfish-demons of the blue depths. Thereafter the Klamaths considered it unlucky even to observe the lake from afar. Almost eighty years after Chief David told this tale, it was retold by June Poitras, a Klamath woman, as "Legend of the Lake" in Gladys Bibee Price's *Te-Yok-Keen (HearYe!)*, published for the La Grande, Oregon, 1962 Indian Festival of the Arts. The recurring idea of dismembering sacrifices to toss from Llao Rock may well recall actual rituals of an earlier race whom the Klamaths, Shastas, and Modocs demonized in their folk lore. According to "A Sketch of Southern Oregon Scenery and Traditions"—written pseudonymously by "Occident" for the August 1877 issue of *The West Shore*—these demons were condemned spirits that had access to the living world through the lake.

Ella E. Clark's "The War Between Lao and Skell" in *Indian Legends of the Pacific Northwest* (1953) retells O. C. Applegate's "Legend of the Llaos" in *Steel Points* (1907, pp. 75–76; given separately from Chief David's Llao legend in the same journal). Captain Applegate, "the sage of Klamath," told this tale around a campfire at Crater Lake when on a camping trip with journalist William Steel and wilderness poet Joaquin Miller. His creative imagination combined Modoc and Klamath versions, with additions and deletions of his own. A more complex version of the legend— the only version I encountered that retained the character of the boyish maiden Chao—is given by Stanton Lapham in his handsome volume *The Enchanted Lake* (1931), the main source for the myth as I've retold it.

Before discovering Lapham's fuller account, I had trouble guessing the deeper purpose of the tale, as such legends are rarely told for the sake of a battle alone. I despaired of being able to retell it myself in a worthwhile manner until I stumbled upon the missing element—the huntress Chao—and immediately recognized the Modoc Earth mother (a woodland huntress) underlying the portrait of the Klamath woman chief. Jeremiah Curtin's *Myths of the Modocs* (1912) describes Latkakawas, Young Earth Mother, as a beautiful blue-colored maiden who dwells on an island in the middle of a lake. Almost certainly, Wizard Island in Crater Lake was intended. With the Earth Mother–like character of Chao restored to the Llao myth, the purpose of the war between the gods Llao and Skell becomes comprehensible: they were rivals for the hand of the boyish maiden who rejected both of them in order to remain with her people as their judge and leader. There is a parallel between this story and that of the Klickitat goddess Loowit (Mount St. Helens) and the war waged between Mounts Hood and Adams after Loowit refused to wed either of them. Loowit and Latkakawas were both capable of appearing to be old hags. "The Crater Lake Myth," collected by Leslie Spier from Robert David in the Klamath language, published in Muhammad Abd-al-Rahman Barker's *Klamath Texts* (1963), likewise contrasts a beautiful maiden with a hag or one-eyed matron, interestingly supposing the matron to be a good wife and the maiden to be dangerous.

We might well ask how the Llao legend ever came to be retold by whites without the critical character of Chao, whose absence reduced a complex myth to a trivial "football" legend highlighted by a game played with Skell's heart and Llao's head (in Robert David's telling, the Klamaths called Crater Lake "The Ball Court"). I can only guess that the beginning, which describes the daughter being trained as a son, was removed because of behavior deemed inappropriate to her gender. Chao the maiden vanishes from the middle of the story if one assumes that Chao the Antelope was just another of Skell's animals, instead of a maiden who got possession of Skell's heart as it passed from Llao's players to those faithful to Skell. The concluding allusions to a woman chief which Lapham preserves had to be left out by authors who thought it incomprehensible that a woman could achieve such a position, even though the historicity of such women is well documented. As Will Roscoe says in the Native American anthology *Living the Spirit* (1988),

"Women became hunters, warriors, mediators, and even chiefs in many tribes of North America. They lived and dressed like men and married other women."

Mark Brickell Kerr's "Legend of Crater Lake" in *Oregon Native Son* (July 1899) is reprinted as "Wiamwita, A Legend of Crater Lake" in *The Pacific Monthly* (October 1901), and there is another version in Lapham's *Enchanted Lake*. This constitutes a Shasta tradition of a lovers' triangle, with characters closely paralleling the dark god Llao, the bright god Skell (or Martin, sometimes regarded as the spirit of Mount Shasta), and the huntress Chao. Young Wiamwita (Grizzly Bear) loved the maiden Tkulucul (Lark). But she believed he cared only for exploits and battles, thus accepted groveling Tsilu (Red Flicker) as her platonic companion. Heartsick Wiamwita made a pilgrimage to Mount Shasta and spoke to old woman Winneshua ("Who Sees Ahead," an elderly Earth Mother). She invested him with power and sent him upon a spirit quest to distant Crater Lake in the land of the Klamaths. The maiden overheard this and, disguising herself as a young hunter, followed her lover. She hunted alone, catching fish and a deer, and bringing these to Wiamwita who had camped in a desolate spot. She insisted upon sharing all his perils. Tracking them stealthily was jealous Tsilu, who, upon hearing the couple's loving words, swore vengeance. At Crater Lake, while Wiamwita underwent ascetic hardships atop Llao Rock, Tsilu set upon him, tossing him into the freezing waters. From the lakeshore, Tkulucul saw her lover fall and leapt in after him, while at the same time the crawfish-demons reared up from the lake to snatch Tsilu from the rock, tearing him to pieces. They made Wizard Island out of his his evil heart. Upon that isle Wiamwita and Tkulucul were saved from drowning, and they dwell there happily to this day.

The huntresses Chao and Tkulucul share the gender-blending

behavior which was the very thing that identified their leadership capacity. Such individuals, of either sex, were called *tw!inna'ek* by the Klamaths, and known popularly by a French-derived term, *berdache*. At first glance it may seem as though Chao's "masculine" traits were assumed for a sexist purpose, as though such capable women are de facto manlike. This is certainly how the story is apt to be received by a modern reader, yet such was *not* its effect in its original context of native society. There are other Northwest tales regarding future chiefs who as young men exhibit feminine traits (see the discussion under "Young Man Who Became Weary"), so it was the androgynous capacity that marked the potential for leadership whether in young men or in young women, a reality that I find both curious and wonderful.

RED WOLF'S DAUGHTER AND BLOODY CHIEF'S SON

Wallowa Lake, at the foot of the Wallowa Mountains of northeastern Oregon, is nearly 300 feet deep. Its name is a Nez Perce word that alludes to fish traps. But the popular meaning is more to the poetic side—"Land of Winding Waters," from Chief Joseph's own description. The Wallowa Mountains constitute Oregon's highest alpine area, with fifteen peaks standing at 9,000-foot elevations. The lake itself is at 4,550 feet and is five miles long, a half-mile wide.

Ella E. Clark, under the heading "The Strange Creatures in Wallowa Lake" in *Indian Legends from the Northern Rockies* (1966), tells of a herd of cattle that dwells in Wallowa Lake (as has also been told of Blue Lake of the Moses Coulee and several other Northwest lakes). Aquatic black bears, giant crabs, and monstrous lobsters are among the weird beings that come out of the lake to snatch people or livestock. A. W. Nelson's *Those Who Came First* (1934), in the chapter "Facts and Fancy," adds information about a giant crawfish (similar to those that serve the demon Llao in Crater Lake) that comes ashore and uses its tail to scoop up mounds of dirt; it's my guess that gargantuan crawfishes were once credited with creating the mountain range in this manner.

By far the most famous of the Wallowa monsters is the lake serpent. There was a saying among the pioneers that Wallowa Lake required one victim a year; an annual drowning was taken for granted. Modern sightings of the monster have been numerous. Grace Bartlet in her pamphlet *The Story of Wallowa Lake* (1967) says, "The legend of the monster persists to this day. Many claim to have seen this creature." Mike Helm in his chapter on the Wallowa Lake monster in *Oregon's Ghosts and Monsters* (1983) tells of lodge owners who saw the beast. He adds that in the 1950s, the corpse of a man drowned in Wallowa Lake was rumored to have washed ashore in Lake Erie!

A version of the Wallowa romance appears in Tom Nash and Twilo Scofield's entertaining *The Well-travelled Casket: A Collection of Oregon Folklife* (1992). Longer versions occur in many books—for example, "Legend of the Beautiful Wallowa Lake," which Reverend R. A. Pollock heard while living among the Nez Perces, was printed in Robert G. Bailey's *River of No Return* (1935). Generally only the couple drowns, although in some versions there is a great battle in the middle of the lake and all the canoes of both tribes are taken under the lake. A poem that serves as a preamble to T. S. Easton's young-adult novel *The Secret of Wallowa Cave* (1934) constitutes a version that more closely resembles the legend of Spirit Lake, Idaho, in which the couple sacrifice themselves by suicide. By contrast, a version in the June 28, 1951, issue of the *Wallowa County Chieftain* supposes pursuers from the two tribes were drowned, but the lovers escaped to live happily ever after. Madge Maynard, who lived at Wallowa, told the closely related variant "Legend of Joseph Lake" in *Oregon Teachers Monthly* (September 1914). This time, only the maiden is drowned. As she was called Wailing Wind, she is perhaps the destructive storm itself. An entirely different legend of Lake Wallowa is given in rhyme by Elva J. Smith as "The Sacrifice" in the *Oregon Teachers Monthly* (September 1912). In this variation the maiden Wild Dove allows herself to be sacrificed at an altar above the lake in order to end war and famine for her people. As far as I am able to judge, the "sacrificial maiden" motif is a popularly versified pioneer alteration of aboriginal motifs (see the discussion of the Multnomah Falls legends, above).

Most printed versions of the tale derive from Chief Joseph's own "A Legend of Wallowa Lake," preserved in George A. Waggoner's *Stories of Old Oregon* (1905). Chief Joseph inherited the Wallowa region from his forebearers and ruled there in peace until the U.S. government demanded the Nez Perces abandon the richly beautiful valley in favor of the harsh Lapwai reservation. General O. O. Howard told a native council that he didn't care about right or wrong; all that mattered was compliance within thirty days, without which he would force the issue by rifle and bayonet. Cornered by unreasoning injustice, Chief Joseph felt he had no choice but to ride at the head of the Wallowa faction in the famous 1878 war. Years later, General Howard admitted the injustice. He said he would rather have assisted white settlers in relocating out of the valley, but he'd felt he had no choice, as he was following orders—a familiar refrain in the Nuremberg trials as well.

Until Chief Joseph's just rebellion, he was on excellent terms with the white immigrants. In 1870, he invited George Waggoner and two of Waggoner's friends to join him and five of his men on a hunt. They caught thirteen elk and took the carcasses to the Nez Perce village. As meat cured over coals, young Chief Joseph, also known as Eagle Wing, told the Wallowa Lake tale to entertain his three guests. He was convinced of the general truth of the narrative, which occurred about 140 years earlier. Assuredly there were Nez Perce chiefs called Red Wolf. Eva Emery Dye in *McLoughlin and Old Oregon* (1900) speaks of a Chief Red Wolf on the Snake River who, after receiving seedlings from early pioneer Henry Spalding, became the first Native American of the Oregon Territory to establish a fruit orchard. When Chief Joseph was asked if the monster, too, was real, he suggested the tragedy had a natural cause, brought about by a sudden storm and a big wave.

LAKE OF THE JEALOUS WOMEN

Beaver women were known in all parts of the Northwest as dwindled goddesses roughly equivalent to the nymphs of Artemis, dangerous to whoever spied upon them. The source of the present retold tale is *Blackfeet Tales of Glacier National Park* (1916), by James Will Schultz, himself a Blackfoot. It is sufficiently "realistic" to have been an actual tragedy, perfectly historical; but it could just as easily be a rationalistic version of a prehistoric myth of a twin goddess of Life and Death, the mythic qualities fading as she/they became reduced to the role of bickering wives. After contact with Catholics, the Blackfeet worshipped the Virgin Mary as Pah-toh-ahk-kee-oh, "The Good Spirit Woman." This Blackfoot Mary, for whom Glacier Park's St. Mary's Lake and St. Mary's River are named, displaced an earlier native Earthmother.

Of the lake to which this legend is attached, James Schultz said, "In my time we called it Beaver Woman's Lake. It is now McDermott Lake. There are names for other lakes and peaks here just as bad as that. Only by an act of Congress can we get what we want done, and we have faith that within a reasonable time all these mountains and lakes and streams will bear names of the great chiefs, medicine men and warriors who traversed them before the white men came." If Congress had proven responsive, McDermott Lake along the Piegan Trail would today be called Lake of the Jealous Women. It is linked by a small creek to Lake Altya in one of the park's most serenely beautiful areas. Mount Gould dominates the backdrop, towering 4,700 feet over McDermott Lake.

SPIRIT OF THE GREY WOLF

Red Fish Lake is a deep, cold lake in Blaine County in southern Idaho, named for the brightly colored strain of sockeye salmon that does not go to sea, but matures in the lake before spawning upstream. The story is retold from a version given as "The Legend of Red Fish Lake; or, The Indians of the Clouds" in Charles Shirley Walgamott's *Six Decades Back* (1936). This is a remarkable collection of firsthand reports of Territorial days, beautifully written before 1927 while the author was between ages sixty and eighty, although there is only the one native legend.

Walgamott received the tale from a Shoshone-Bannock woman whom he called Indian Mary. In 1875, this woman had a private camp in a shady grotto at Rock Creek in southern Idaho. Her two wikiups were covered in buffalo hides decorated with hunting scenes painted in blue and red. She made her living preparing skins and manufacturing gloves, moccasins, and beaded buckskins, which she sold and traded to cowboys and immigrants.

Walgamott was a teenager at the time, fresh off the stagecoach at Rock Creek, Idaho Territory, a station along the Oregon Trail. He won his way into Mary's confidence and was told the present legend, though by the time he put it in writing he'd had several decades to embellish the incidents, incorporating such "asides" as the origin of the name "Idaho," which probably was not included in Mary's original. Mary had learned the story from her Bannock mother (her father was a Shoshone warrior). Her mother claimed to be a witness of the events in her own girlhood.

It may well be a partly historical tale regarding the origin of the so-called Sheepeater Indians, "sheepeaters" being a pioneer designation for certain bands of Snakes, Shoshones, or Bannocks who hunted wild mountain sheep.

THE MYSTERIOUS HERMIT OF LITTLE FALLS

The Little Falls hermit of the St. Joe Valley in Idaho was a real person. Ruth Bennet Keeton writes of him in the article "The Hermit of Little Falls" for the Summer 1973 issue of *Incredible Idaho*. Every element of his character, as represented in the present short story, is in keeping with Keeton's portrait. Her article includes a photograph of the hermit, who looks a bit like Walt Whitman in his later years, standing in the front of a boat, giving a ride to a woman who had visited the falls. The story's blue rose is my small conceit, incorporating the mythic symbol of the Romanticist movement, for which the blue rose was an emblem of perfect, unachievable beauty.

THE SHINBONE STAFF

This is a retelling of the Clatsop Indian story "The Legend of the Surf," as it was titled within Silas B. Smith's article "Primitive Customs and Religious Beliefs of the Indians of the Pacific Northwest Coast" in the *Quarterly of the Oregon Historical Society* (September 1901). The legend was superficially retold by Jim Martin as "Indian Legend Explains Why Ocean Roars" in the Sunday *Oregonian* (December 13, 1976).

Silas Smith was of the tribe that formerly lived at the mouth of the Necanicum River, where the story is set. His mother, Celiast, daughter of Chief Kobaiway of the Clatsops, was Silas's authority on her people's folkways and legends; her personal heroism is recounted in H. S. Lyman's "The Story of Celiast" in the *Pacific Monthly* (February

1900). The Clatsop nation began at the southern mouth of the Columbia River running southward along the coast to the Necanicum, after which the country became increasingly dominated by the Tillamooks. This expanse of Oregon coastline was noted for the ferocity of its storms and currents, with many trade ships lost upon the shores. It was natural enough for native mythology to assume a Seatco was at work in the deadly surf.

The cedar board engraved with ribs, as encountered in this story, was an actual fetish object, the exact importance of which has long been forgotten. Anthropologists have suggested that these were used in ancestral ghost religion, a surmise derived from their deathly appearance. What is more likely is that such fetishes were displayed in longhouses, but without the religious importance of ancestral ghosts; rather, the boards were intended to appease evil spirits such as the Seatco. In *Narrative of a Journey Across the Rocky Mountains to the Columbia River* (1839), John Townsend—the antihero of "Ghoul John and the Corpse" in this collection—was informed by Chief Chinamus that whenever he felt himself under an evil spell, he placed himself against the plank-idol until the difficulty passed. Townsend noted that such a crude and "uncouth figure" was never addressed as a deity. Older ones were unceremoniously discarded among rubbish.

THE WOMAN WHOSE HUSBAND WAS A SEAL

This tale draws mainly from three versions collected by ethnographers in or near Coos Bay, Oregon. "The Wife of Seal," from Melville Jacobs's *Coos Myth Texts* (1940), was told in about 1933 by Annie Miner Peterson of the Coos tribe, when she was elderly and frail. Two earlier versions appeared in Leo J. Frachtenberg's and Harry Hull St. Clair's *Coos Texts* (1913). Foremost is "The Woman Who Married the Seal," which gives different scenes of the same story told by Annie Peterson. The third version is "The Woman Who Married the Merman," which also has several overlapping scenes.

A related tale, "The Boy Who Went to Live with the Seals," from Edward Sapir and Jeremiah Curtin's *Wasco Tales and Myths* (1909), also impacted my retelling. This is a close parallel, although the protagonist is a feral child rather than someone of marriageable age. He lives amidst the seals at the mouth of the Columbia River. He is captured by his family and forcibly brought home, but is returned to the seals at the first opportunity. Sapir notes that the story, though told by the Wascos up the Columbia, "is a characteristic type of tale or myth among the Coos." In all these versions the seals provide a better clan life than do humans.

The Tillamooks, who dwelt along the coast north of the Coos, told the story with a touch of horror rather than romance. Tillamooks supposed seals to be dangerous because of their lust for human mates. In "The Man Who Was Husband to a Seal" in Elizabeth Derr Jacobs's *Nehalem Tillamook Tales* (1959), a married man, saved from drowning by a seal, was kept by the seal as her husband. He then took other seal wives as well. After a long time, he escaped and returned to his human wife and daughter. He was thereafter afraid of water. When he finally had the nerve the go fishing in the sea, his seal wives saw and reclaimed him. Although the Tillamook version is a more dispirited legend than that of the Coos, the mythic importance is the same. These tales convey the sentiment that men or women lost to the sea do not die, but become wedded to it, functioning thereafter as protective guardians or intermediaries between humans and those races of animals a tribe may hunt for food. The little aside of Maiden Tears Grotto on the South Coos River was a legend reported in Charlotte L. Mahaffy's *Coos River Echoes* (1965).

WILD VOYAGE OF THE STEAMSHIP *DORA*

I've retold this tale from a version given by George Kosmos of Roino, Greece, who came to Californa as a very young man and soon after went to Alaska during the Nilshina gold rush. Sourdoughs were notorious for their tall tales, but the miraculous adventures of the steamship *Dora* seem not to have been much exaggerated, if at all, when Kosmos wrote it up as "*Dora . . . The Sailing Ship That Came Home*" for his collection of witty adventures in *Alaska Sourdough Stories* (1956). Special thanks are extended to yachtsman Grant Fjermedal for going over my version for nautical accuracy and for adding some descriptive passages of waters he has visited.

THE DOOR TO RAINMAKER'S LODGE

Stanley Park, in the city of Vancouver, British Columbia, was formerly the home of the Squamish people. The shore beneath the Lion's Gateway, the location of the present legend, was the cultural center of the tribe. The tale is retold from a version given by B. A. McKelvie as "Si'atmuulth, the Rainmaker" in *Legends of Stanley Park: Vancouver's Magnificent Playground* (1941).

The Squamish Rainmaker legend is typical of several tribal tales that assign to a certain man or woman the capacity to control the rain by opening and closing a lodge door or some other means. Such stories are generally told of mortals with shamanic capacity, yet often with hints of their having been a Rain-god or Rain-goddess. A legend collected in Oregon, for example, tells of a black woman who adopted Indian ways and became a shaman. Her emotional states decided the weather. If she wept, there was rain; if she laughed, there was sunlight. There are other rainmaker legends, as would be expected in Northwest environs, though in the present retelling I have adhered fairly closely to the Squamish myth.